Poetry with Pleasure

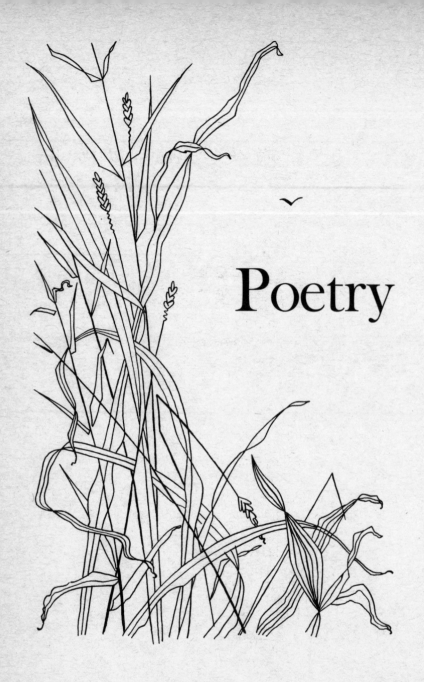

Poetry

LAURENCE A. KIRKPATRICK

Head of the English Department
Hawthorne High School
Hawthorne, California

WILLIAM W. GOODFELLOW

Coordinator, Honors Program in Humanities
Centinela Valley Union High School District
Hawthorne, California

with Pleasure

Decorations by James and Ruth McCrea

CHARLES SCRIBNER'S SONS, NEW YORK

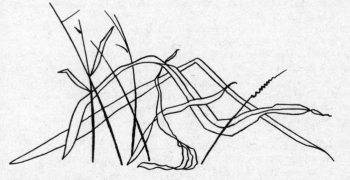

5 7 9 11 13 15 17 19   M/P   20 18 16 14 12 10 8 6

Printed in the United States of America
Library of Congresss Catalog Card Number 65-12301

ISBN 0-684-51533-4

The editors wish to thank the following authors, publishers and other holders of copyright for permission to use copyrighted materials:

Esther Root Adams, Executrix of the Estate of Franklin P. Adams, for "Those Two Boys" by Franklin P. Adams.

Mrs. Berton Braley, Executrix of the Estate of Berton Braley, for "Opportunity" by Berton Braley.

The Caxton Printers, Ltd., Caldwell, Idaho, for "Cave" from *Collected Poems* by Glenn Ward Dresbach. Used by special permission of the copyright owners.

Zafer Cetinkaya, Istanbul, Turkey, for "On an old oak tree."

Chatto & Windus Ltd., London, England, for Canadian rights to "Lone Dog" from *Songs to Save a Soul* by Irene R. McLeod.

The Confraternity of Christian Doctrine, Washington, D. C., for verses from the book of *Isaias*, Chapter 35, *The Holy Bible*, Confraternity edition.

Country Life Ltd., London, England, for "Dawn" by Isobel Butchart.

Coward-McCann, Inc., New York, N. Y., for "Daniel Webster's Horses" from *The Creaking Stair* by Elizabeth Coatsworth. Copyright 1923 by Elizabeth Coatsworth. Copyright, 1929, 1949 by Coward-McCann, Inc.; for "A Lady Comes to the Inn" from *Compass Rose* by Elizabeth Coatsworth. Copyright 1929 by Coward-McCann, Inc.

J. M. Dent & Sons Ltd., London, England, for Canadian rights to "The Donkey" by G. K. Chesterton.

DeSylva, Brown and Henderson, Inc., New York, N. Y., for two lines from *September Song*. Copyright © 1938 by DeSylva, Brown and Henderson, Inc. Copyright renewed.

Dodd, Mead & Company, Inc., New York, N. Y., for "The Sea Gypsy" from *More Songs From Vagabondia* by Richard Hovey; for American rights to "The Cremation of

Susan M. Stevens, Lafayette, California, for "Harvest."

Edith Swain, Tucson, Arizona, for "Wild Mares Running" by Frank Swain.

The Society of Authors, London, England, and the Literary Trustees of Walter de la Mare, for "The Listeners," "Sam," "Silver," "The Sleeper," "Someone," and "All But Blind" by Walter de la Mare; The Society of Authors as the literary representative of the Estate of the late Richard Le Gallienne for Canadian rights to "I Meant to Do My Work Today" by Richard Le Gallienne.

Texas Review, Dallas, Texas, for "A Summer Night" by George D. Bond, published in the *Texas Review,* Vol. VIII, 1922 by the Southern Methodist University Press.

The Viking Press, Inc., New York, N. Y., for American rights to "Lone Dog" from *Songs to Save A Soul* by Irene Rutherford McLeod. All rights reserved; for "The Sky" from *Under the Tree* by Elizabeth Madox Roberts. Copyright 1922 by B. W. Huebsch Inc., 1950 by Ivor S. Roberts.

The World Publishing Company, New York, N. Y., for a selection from *Letters of Emily Dickinson,* ed. Mabel Loomis Todd. Copyright 1951 by the World Publishing Company.

Mr. M. B. Yeats and the Macmillan Co. of Canada Ltd. for Canadian rights to "When You Are Old" from *Collected Poems* by William Butler Yeats.

Introduction

Poetry with Pleasure is the culmination of seven years of preparation and experimentation. In 1958, a committee of English teachers from the Centinela Valley Union High School District, Hawthorne, California, was asked to prepare a comprehensive English Course of Study for its four metropolitan high schools. The committee soon found that many vital segments of the English curriculum were deficient in textbook materials, but particularly disappointing were the standard anthologies that included poetry sections within their many pages. Accordingly, our committee began to try out various poems of our own selection in our classes.

After several years of classroom testing, we felt we had collected a good variety of classic and modern poems that had shown themselves time and again to have significant meaning to our students. Our trial and error experimentation had demonstrated that there is a universality of poetic appreciation not limited to age or grade level.

As our collection of poems grew, we also became aware of other basic needs for the appreciation of poetry. Students had little understanding of the origins and purposes of poetry; many of poetry's greatest charms—its conciseness, its appeal to the intuition, its richness of language—were obscured by the students' prosaic vision. Furthermore, little had been written on the students' level to assist them in interpretation; such terms as "symbolism" and "allusion" were almost meaningless to young readers, as were various literary devices of the poet—metaphor, personification, simile, for example. Missing also was a simplified yet lucid explanation of metrics which could give added insight into poems and poetic effects. As these needs became apparent to us, we prepared our own material to satisfy them.

We also discovered that students like to write poetry and that even their untrained efforts produce surprisingly good results. We became increasingly aware that student poetic impulses can be encouraged and accelerated through appropriate guidance at the right moment; a gentle but timely nudge toward proper writing techniques often brought rich rewards. The type and nature of these "nudges" were recorded and tested, and the final chapter of *Poetry with Pleasure* includes, we believe, thoughtful guidance for would-be-poets in their writing efforts.

In summary, then, this book has been planned so that students may find pleasure in some very fine poems, acquire a degree of true insight, become acquainted with the techniques and purposes of the poet's craft, and make a beginning in the writing of original verse. We earnestly hope that this book will provide many gratifying experiences to the teachers who use it, and that their students will always remember *Poetry with Pleasure*.

This book reflects the conscious and unconscious assistance of a great number of students, teachers, and interested colleagues, to whom the authors extend their gratitude. In singling out the following individuals to mention by name, we are at the same time thanking the many people whose contributions may have been less direct but hardly less valuable.

Of particular help to us in choosing poems appropriate and meaningful to young people were the high school notebooks of Elizabeth Goodfellow. These notebooks contain several hundred poems which moved her, as a young girl, to such delight that she transcribed them into a personal anthology when she was the very age of the students to whom this book is primarily directed. Moreover, during the preparation of the book, Mrs. Goodfellow's wide knowledge of poetry and, as a librarian, of literary sources added greatly to the variety of our final selections.

In the obtaining of permissions to reprint the more than one hundred and fifty poems contained in the following pages, the dedicated, often exhausting efforts of Margretta Kirkpatrick deserve our sympathetic and unqualified gratitude. The frustrating job of reducing the original draft of the book to typed manuscript form also fell to her willing hands.

To Mrs. Ada Robacker, Chairman of the English Department of White Plains High School, White Plains, New York; to Albert K. Ridout, Chairman of the English Department of Pelham High School, Pelham, New York; and to Marsden V. Dillenbeck, Chairman of the English Department of Rye High School, Rye, New York our gratitude is due for their thoughtful suggestions leading to the improvement of the original manuscript. Especially do we thank Mrs. Robacker, who followed up her first encouraging review with additional valuable commentary during revision.

The authors wish also to extend their sincere thanks to Paul L. Millane, of the School Department of Charles Scribner's Sons, New York, and to O. C. Keesey, Charles Scribner's Sons, Western Division.

For the preparation of the final manuscript, we gratefully acknowledge the thoughtful, immaculate typing of Mr. James Pressler, and thanks must go also to Miss Diane Guindon, who reviewed the manuscript from the point of view of the student reader.

Finally, and because whatever merit *Poetry with Pleasure* has is due in large measure to the excellence of the poems it contains, our deepest gratitude is reserved for the poets, the copyright owners, and publishers for permission to reprint certain poems in this book.

Contents

IV. Young People

V. The Strange and Supernatural

VI.   Personal Belief

VII.   Humor

VIII. *Reflections*

IX. *Nature*

X. Beyond the Words

XI. Write It Yourself

Poetry with Pleasure

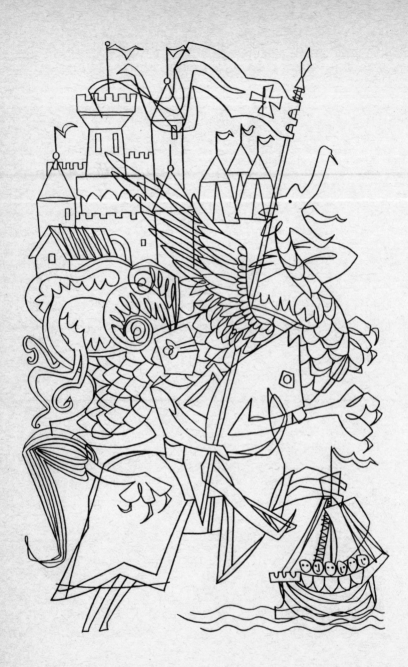

CHAPTER ONE
What Poetry Is

For a moment or two we are going to step backward in time more than 1200 years. We are seated in the great warrior-hall of a powerful English nobleman. It is evening, and our meal, cooked on the long hearth, is now over. The bearded fighters, scarred veterans of many a struggle with shield and broadsword, are deep in their favorite pastime: telling battle stories. Stirring tales of individual duels and conflicts, of dangerous boar and bear hunts, of witches and demons, of great heroes and murderous traitors fill the smoky air.

Soon comes a sharp knock on the door. A tall, leather-clad man strides into the room, a stringed instrument like a guitar under one arm. He smiles at the warriors, tells a joke or two, accepts the meat and drink offered him, and, after eating, moves to the front of the hall to the low platform on which the nobles sit. The talk dies down; all the men are now watching him. He plucks at the strings as the firelight plays across his face. Finally he is ready, and coaxing the proper background music from the instrument, he plunges into his thrilling story. His voice is strong and full of melody, and he sings about a master hero, a strong youth named Beowulf, who fought dragons and demons. His songs, accompanied by the rhythmic strumming of his instrument, fill the hall.

Beowulf is indeed a great fighter, and the stories of his exploits take two hours to tell. The warriors listen; their strong imaginations carry them through every battle of the hero. Eventually all the demons and dragons are dead, Beowulf grows old and dies, and the singer ends his tale. The listeners applaud as the reigning noble, the liege lord, rewards the singer with a gift, perhaps a ring or gold piece. Tomorrow he may travel to another stronghold, there to sing his stories again. He need not worry if the lord of the next realm is unfriendly with the lord of this one, for the singer is the "scop," the bearer of tales, and he is welcome anywhere. He is also one of the first poets of the Old English language, although he can neither read nor write. Sitting a little apart from the scop and his rough-and-ready listeners, however, is a very rare person who *can* read and write, and he has copied down almost the entire tale as the scop sang it. This nearly magical act of writing was extremely important to the history of our literature: (1) it "caught" the exact language of the singer on paper, and (2) it marked the official, written beginning of English poetry.

You may still read (in a modern version) the great story of Beowulf as the scop sang it, and as the writer recorded it. As the centuries passed, the language of that early day changed a great deal, and now only scholars can read *Beowulf* in its original form. There are two important lessons to be learned from this very early English poetry, and you might well keep them in mind: (1) the first English poets were master story tellers who thrilled people with their stories and tales, and (2) poetry itself was intended to be sung or spoken.

This English scene of scop and writer we have just observed by no means represents the origin of poetry. Ancient, widely-scattered lands such as Greece, China, Egypt, and India had sizable amounts of poetry in written form long before Beowulf's time. The composition of poetry has apparently been a basic urge of all people. If today you were to visit primitive tribes in little-known areas of the world, you would find that they have certain chants, rituals, and tribal legends which the entire group knows by heart, and it is easy to visualize how a similar pattern existed in all early societies. You know, too, that the use of poetry is commonplace with all children; listen to the child as he plays on the sidewalk:

> Step on a crack,
> Break your mother's back!

With the careful recording of the songs of the scops a new feature was added to the language, giving the English poets a wonderful advantage they had never before enjoyed: their original creations were given a permanency—no longer was it through memory alone that the stories were kept alive. The songs and tales were set down in lasting form so that all the world could one day know them. Although reading them silently is hardly an adequate substitute for the

scop's dramatic recitations, it does make them available for the enjoyment of everyone with the imagination to bring them to life again.

As time went on, the popularity of the scops declined; the warriors
disappeared, and different types of poetry replaced the old battle
tales. Other people wanted to hear songs about their own feelings,
experiences, and interests; and so poems about love, nature, adventure, and other topics were composed and often set to music. Very
important among these early poems were the "popular ballads,"
usually about love, violent death, and romantic adventure. They are
the ancestors to the love ballads so widely sung today on radio and
television. Our modern folk songs and the western "country" songs
are two direct descendants of these early poems.

WHAT POETRY IS

If you were asked to define exactly what poetry is, you would soon
give it up as an almost impossible job. The minute you had said that
poetry must have this or that special quality, you would promptly
discover a poem that did *not* fill the requirement.

Poetry does, however, seem to have one clear characteristic: it has
rhythm. Probably the poems you know best have regular, easily felt
rhythm very similar to the rhythmic beat of music. You know that
dance music has a pattern of heavy and light beats, and the good
dancer moves in accordance with the rhythmic pattern established
by these beats. Just as the composer carefully arranges his notes, so
does the poet carefully place his words in such a way that a regular
pattern of light and heavy beats is produced. Consider these lines,
written by the poet John Dryden:

> Here lies my wife; here let her lie.
> Now she's at rest, and so am I.
> (ta-TUM, ta-TUM, ta-TUM, ta-TUM)
> (ta-TUM, ta-TUM, ta-TUM, ta-TUM)

You can easily see that the beat, or "accent," of the first word is
light, the second heavy, and so on throughout the two lines. The

particular way in which these accents are arranged into a regular pattern is referred to as the "meter" of the poem. Usually a poet will use the same meter throughout his poem, although he may vary it slightly here and there to avoid making it so regular that it grows monotonous.

Rhythm, then, is an essential in poetry. It is necessary to add, however, that not all poets choose to write in such regular, metrical patterns as the one illustrated in the example above. There is in language a very delicate "natural" rhythm that skilled writers can feel and that they sometimes use in a type of poetry known as "free verse." Free verse does not follow precisely the same rules as metrical poetry. The reader is aware, however, of the subtle "rightness" of the way in which the poet has expressed his thoughts, much as a listener is aware that a certain arrangement of notes has produced a true and memorable melody. Here is an example of free verse, taken from a longer poem by Walt Whitman:

> On the beach at night,
> Stands a child with her father,
> Watching the east, the autumn sky.

You will immediately see that there is no "ta-TUM" pattern to this excerpt, but you may sense, without being able to say how or why, that the word arrangement creates an effect both rhythmic and poetic. More will be said about this interesting technique in Chapter Ten and Chapter Eleven.

Rhythm seems to be the only clear-cut, easily detectable characteristic of poetry, for a poem certainly does not need to rhyme or to have an unusual or "fancy" vocabulary. The writer may shorten or lengthen the poem as he wishes, and he may also use as many words in a line as he pleases, providing he does not forget to follow the basic rhythm he has established for himself.

What seems most important about poetry is that it creates a "speaking picture" of some thing or event more effectively and quickly than does prose (that is, the ordinary language of speech or writing). For example, one might say in prose:

Open the gates of the palace

but in poetic form it might be

Swing wide the oaken barriers of the great.

The first statement is a simple order; the second suggests far more than just the opening of a gate. You immediately know, from the poetic speech, that the gates are oaken, and thus rich, strong, and awe-inspiring; you are aware, too, that these barriers usually have the duty of keeping ordinary people out—that this is a special occasion; you realize also, from "Swing wide," a far better picture of the actual opening of the gates. Finally, "the great" brings to mind thoughts of nobility and power, suggesting the gulf between the great high-born nobles inside the castle and the lesser people outside.

You might choose to call poetic speech a fresh, original manner of describing things or events. Poetry is basically a rich, colorful way of speaking. Three devices of language that poets often use to make their observations clear and forceful are *similes, metaphors,* and *personifications.*

These three terms may sound complicated, but they are really simple. You use similes and metaphors constantly, personifications occasionally. A *simile* is the comparison of one thing with another to give emphasis and color to a statement, as "He hits the line like a bulldozer," or "He ran as fast as lightning." Notice that a simile uses *like* or *as* to make its comparison.

A *metaphor* is also a comparison, but it does its job without *like* or *as.* These are metaphors: "He was a tiger on defense" and "She was a jewel."

Personification means giving the qualities of a person to a thing or idea; for example, "The sun watched the children playing" or "The wind screamed and growled through the night." The sun does not "watch" or the wind "scream," but your imagination accepts the images and you achieve more vivid pictures as a result.

You use the three figures of speech almost every day; so does the poet, but because of his keen awareness and imagination he often creates fresh, original figures of unusual clarity. To put it another way, the poet employs the same "tricks" of speech as you use when you wish to emphasize a point, but his are usually more striking. By being original, both in perception and expression, he can capture your interest. He is able, by using these imaginative touches, to give added emphasis and depth to his observations.

POETRY HAS ADVANTAGES OVER PROSE

You discovered long ago that when you write a composition the words don't flow out exactly as you wish they would. How many times have you said, "I know what I want to say, but I just can't say it"? You wish to be clear and interesting as you write, but too often your results are dull, incomplete, or inexact in meaning. You must rewrite or rephrase, trying again and again to put down your thoughts as you feel they should be stated. Think then, of the enormous skill required of the poet, who, restricted to a minimum of words and confined to a pattern for these words, must achieve all the clarity of expression you work for, as well as suggest many ideas beyond what is stated.

To understand the suggestive power of poetry, suppose for a minute that you were asked to describe how fog comes in over a harbor town at night; how it moves in stealthily and silently, settles in valleys and hollows, becomes thicker and more dense as the night passes; and finally, with the coming sun, how it dissolves into nothingness. Observe how Carl Sandburg, the noted American poet, describes fog in a coastal scene:

FOG

> The fog comes
> on little cat feet.
>
> It sits looking
> over harbor and city
> on silent haunches
> and then moves on.

If you are a perceptive reader, you have noticed that Sandburg suggests more with his short poem than does the long sentence preceding it. You may have felt the silence that fog imposes on a city, and you perhaps have wondered where it went as it lifted. Sandburg's use of this fog-as-cat idea has provided you with a mental picture and has suddenly increased your understanding. You immediately see fog in terms of the characteristic movements of a cat, and your imagination quickly supplies additional similarities. Poetry, then, *suggests* rather than describes; and if the poetry is of high quality, you gain—often very quickly—a deeper awareness and understanding than you usually receive from prose.

Another way in which poetry is often superior to prose is in lending freshness to ordinary, everyday ideas. Consider, for example, the advice that well-meaning people give you concerning the problems of life. All this helpful information may be perfectly good, but it has probably been repeated to you with so little variation that you hardly hear it any more. Notice, then, the freshness of Delmore Schwartz's words when he says:

> Time is the school in which we learn,
> Time is the fire in which we burn.

His ideas are not new, but there is an originality in how they are expressed that makes you listen to what he is saying and see the truth of his words.

Many of you may have the popular notion that the poets are a separate race of people, dwelling apart from humanity, living on the beaches and in attics, letting their hair grow long, existing on handouts and scraps of bread, and generally withdrawing from civilization. Perhaps a few poets do have some of these peculiarities, but the great majority of poets are much like you. They look like the people you know, wear the same types of clothes, and have good and bad points, just as everyone else. It is a mistake to accept any set idea about poets as a special class of people. There are many poets who lead very regular lives, achieve a fine old age, and have good marriages and many children and grandchildren. The famous English poets Wordsworth, Tennyson, and Browning all lived calmly to an advanced age. In America, Robert Frost was a good example: at eighty-eight he was still healthy, was still composing fine poetry and leading the same quiet life he had always preferred. On the other hand, there have been poets who led most dramatic lives, sometimes dying tragically, as did Keats, Byron, and Shelley. Poets should not be judged as a class any more than should other people.

There are, however, some distinct qualities which poets possess that not all people have. Poets have highly active imaginations, are especially sympathetic and sensitive toward others, and are particularly good observers of the life about them. Naturally, these qualities are found in many people, not simply in poets. There is no denying, however, that poets *do* love words and enjoy experimenting with language far more than do most people. It is probable that some of your classmates possess all these qualities, and the chances are that they could write fine poetry.

It is interesting to realize that today most poets do not rely on their poetry to make a living. As a rule they have regular jobs, often in some type of work that gives them knowledge and background for their writing. Robert Frost, a farmer for many years, could describe New England farm life with great accuracy; Carl Sandburg, in his younger years a harvest worker in the Midwest, captures the heat and action of harvest-time in his poetry; William Carlos Williams, a doctor, wrote poetry reflecting his knowledge and understanding of sickness, death, and the miracle of life. All three men used their occupational experience to develop the insight which makes their poetry so rewarding to read.

Often poetry is intended solely for the writer's personal pleasure or for that of his friends. Many excellent poems in various books have no author's name attached to them; you cannot tell who wrote them, or when the writing was done. Emily Dickinson, now considered by many people to have been America's finest poetess, thought it quite improper to have her poetry printed. Most of her verse was found after her death, and in her will she had left orders that all her writings should be burned. Luckily for the world, her wish was disregarded, permitting everyone to read her poems. There have doubtless been many Emily Dickinsons whose fine poems perished with them. Poetry, you must realize, is basically a personal experience for the writer, and it may be unimportant to him whether or not anyone ever reads it.

WHAT KIND OF POETRY SHOULD YOU LIKE?

It would be foolish for anyone to say that you should like *all* poetry. It is sensible, however, to say that you will probably like *certain types* of poetry. To a person who loves nature, a poem dealing with the out-of-doors is likely to be appealing. This same person might have little interest in a poem about an unfamiliar or, to him, distasteful subject—war, for example. The poets themselves have never altogether agreed on what poetry a person should like. They have often been in such disagreement that some of their comments on one another's poetry have been very unpleasant. When the poets themselves differ so widely in their viewpoints, it is hardly surprising to find disagreements among their readers concerning what is "good" or "bad" poetry. What you should and will like is largely a matter of your own personal taste.

The subject matter the individual poet chooses for his poetry is just as personal as your taste for his poems. He writes what he wishes. Generally, however, a poet tends to fall into one of two main groups. He may prefer to write *intellectual* poetry: that is, poetry which concerns itself with matters of the mind and soul, perhaps in the examination of the serious problems in life. He may, on the other hand, write *descriptive* poetry: that is, fine descriptions of places and events that are interesting in themselves without obvious reference to the complex nature of life itself. A few poets, Shakespeare, for example, are at home with both intellectual and descriptive verse, often blending the two. You may like the intellectual poems and not be interested in the descriptive; or the reverse may be true. You may very well like both types. In any event, there is poetry available to suit your tastes and interests.

HOW MAY YOU LEARN TO UNDERSTAND POETRY BETTER?

A large number of poems are written in such a way that they are easy to comprehend. Most humorous poems, such as those in Chapter Seven, seem to be easily understood; actually they are no easier than other types; it is your appreciation of humor that makes them appear simpler than the others.

Occasionally, however, you will find a poem that is difficult to understand, one in which you are not sure what the writer is trying to express. Frequently a poet writes to satisfy his own desires for self-expression, and he takes shortcuts in his wording, or he packs a great deal of thought into a few brief lines. As a result, the meaning of the poem is not clear to you as you read it. There are several steps you may find helpful in gaining an understanding of such poems more quickly:

Read difficult poems aloud. Do this several times if necessary. Often a poem contains a difficult passage where the poet's mind moved too fast for you to follow easily, and you may realize the meaning as you say his words aloud. Problem areas in meaning tend to disappear as you speak the poem, especially in those cases where a sentence runs through several lines.

Learn the poetic symbols that most poets use. Writers of poetry are fond of using words that have more than one meaning. When a poet speaks of the seasons, for example, he may mean not only the time of year but also the time of life. Thus spring can mean the youthful period of life; summer, manhood and early maturity; fall, middle age; and winter, old age and approaching death. Colors are often symbolic: the dark many times means evil, and light indicates goodness; thus a raven may suggest evil; an albatross, good. The sea and its terms may be symbolic: a voyage indicates the journey of life; a harbor, the goal or end of that journey; a reef, difficulties along the way. There are countless symbols taken from all areas of existence that serve this dual function.

Read other poems by the same poet. Usually a writer has several key ideas that are very important to him. These ideas are beliefs that have had great influence on his life. As a consequence, he returns to them in one way or another many times in different poems. A favorite idea of A. E. Housman's is that youth is the best period of life and that the individual who dies young is fortunate to be spared the disillusionments of old age. Having found this idea expressed in one of Housman's poems, you should read other poems by him, prepared to see this important idea restated.

WHAT MAKES A POEM A GOOD POEM?

Saying that one poem is "good" or that another is "poor" is a dangerous thing to do. To pass judgment on a poem as "good" or "poor" is to forget a very important factor: poems, just as people, have individual differences. Calling one poem "good" and insisting that other readers label it in the same manner is similar to expecting all people to have the same personal tastes, opinions, and experiences. Clearly what is "good" to one person may be something different to another, both in life and in poetry.

It is true that there are some poems that the majority of people enjoy, and the collection of poems in this book includes a large number of these favorites. Still, you would be a strange person indeed if you liked all of them or if, on the other hand, you disliked every one. It is possible, too, that you will find certain parts of a poem to your liking and yet find other sections of the same poem that you do not care for. Poets, as well the most experienced readers, disagree as to what is a "good" poem, and few people will completely agree on a list of "favorite poems."

There is no doubt that some poems do have a special, powerful appeal to certain readers. Exactly what this appeal is cannot be explained. There seems to be a unique magic in poetic language that can stimulate a reader enormously, and it is difficult to determine how this stimulation is accomplished. There are times when you do know how the poet has created his effect: it may be his ability to put into clear words thoughts of your own, thoughts that you believed belonged solely to your private world of dreams. Suddenly you discover a person well acquainted with this dreamland who can describe it in unforgettable words. Sometimes the writer is speaking of something that has happened to both you and him, putting into language the emotions you experienced at the time. The appeal certain poems have for you may be explained by the poet's ability to tell a good story, as did the ancient *Beowulf* scop. Whatever the reasons are—and certainly there are more than have been listed here —poetry can bring about a powerful effect on the reader.

There is a strong similarity between the enjoyment of music and the enjoyment of poetry. Some people are moved by popular songs of the love-ballad variety; others prefer faster music, perhaps with a strong beat; and still others enjoy classical music most. You may like all three, but it is a rare person who does not have his favorite songs. Similarly, some of the poems in this book will move you emotionally; while others will produce little or no effect, but it is likely that you will develop a list of special favorites, those that speak to you most deeply and clearly.

What happens to you when you first read a poem depends upon you as an individual. One thing is extremely clear: it is seldom that a person can fully appreciate a new poem the first time he hears it. The average person may learn to understand it completely in due time, just as he learns to enjoy a new song; but the chances are that he must reread or listen to the poem several times before he grasps the full value of it. In poetry, deep appreciation emerges only with familiarity. If you should happen to be one of those rare people who can receive the full emotional effect of poetry at first reading, you are very lucky. One such sensitive person was Emily Dickinson; she analyzed and described her reactions in this manner:

> If I read a book and it makes my whole body
> so cold no fire can ever warm me, I know that
> is poetry. If I feel physically as if the top of my
> head were taken off, I know that is poetry.
> These are the only ways I know it. Is there any
> other way?

Perhaps you may never feel as intensely as Miss Dickinson; but it is possible that you can learn to feel more deeply than you ever have before. There is depth in all people; and if you will let your own sensitivity develop, you can extend your capacity for understanding and awareness far beyond that which you now enjoy.

ENJOYING POETRY

To enjoy poetry then, you should approach it in much the same way you begin a new sport or hobby. The poetry should be "tried out" before you make decisions about it. Be wary of those people who want to convince you that a particular poem is "good" and that "you should like it." Even if you enjoy only a few of all the poems you read, you will find that these few will provide lifelong pleasure.

Poetry can produce a strong response in you as you learn to understand it. A poem such as Kipling's "If" or Henley's "Invictus" may give you inspiration or a burst of courage just when you need it. A humorous poem may tap your sense of fun enough to brighten up a dismal day; a well-told tale in verse may lift you far above the cares of the world. And remember, if the so-called "good" poems have little meaning for you, don't be discouraged; for just as you find all kinds of short stories and novels to read and enjoy, so, too, will you find all types of poems.

Keep in mind that the poets themselves are vital, interesting people. Their imagination and sensitivity often let them see things more clearly than you do, and it is precisely these qualities which make their ideas so entertaining and meaningful. Read their poems aloud several times; do not be afraid to put aside a poem if it lacks appeal, or to express approval if it seems good to you; and make an honest effort to learn some of the poets' short cuts—their use of symbols, their imagery, and their rich words. Above all, read widely. A whole lifetime of enjoyment awaits you.

CHAPTER TWO

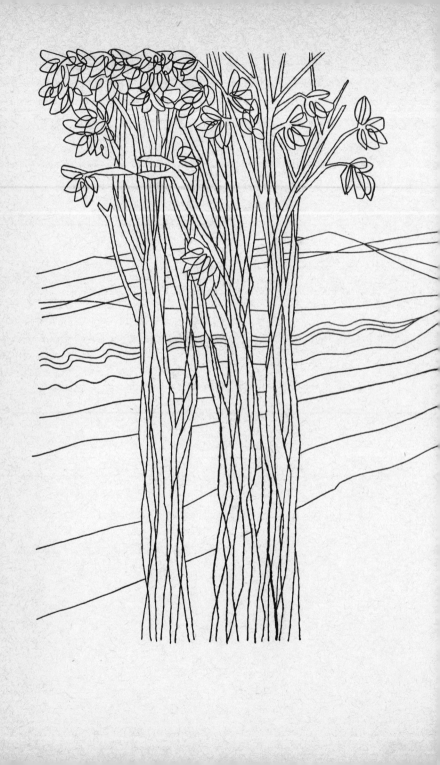

Enjoying Poetry More

The wind was a torrent of darkness among the gusty trees.
The moon was a ghostly galleon tossed upon cloudy seas.
The road was a ribbon of moonlight over the purple moor,
And the highwayman came riding—
　　Riding—riding—
The highwayman came riding, up to the old inn-door.

FROM "THE HIGHWAYMAN," BY ALFRED NOYES

How much imagination do you have? Move across the worn oaken floor and look out the high, narrow window. What do you see? You are in an old English inn that sits alone, deserted, surrounded by dark, tall trees which bend and groan as the strong wind tears at them. There are no friendly lights out in the darkness, only the faint glow of the moon, which now and then shines brilliantly through the broken clouds. The moonlight reflects from the highway as it twists and turns across the moor; for the dark foliage on both sides of the road makes it a silver thread across a purple fabric. Far away, a figure appears on the road. As it draws closer, you see it is a horseman. He seems almost a ghost rider, jet black in the distance. You lose him for a moment or two; and then, as he draws nearer and as the moonlight brightens, you can make him out more clearly. At last he is in full view, galloping toward the inn itself. The moon is now a spotlight; the rider and his horse are the central figures on the stage. He is important but mysterious, not yet flesh and blood; he is still too much a part of the night, the road, and the darkness to have a personality. Suddenly, the drumming of the horse's hoofs sound his arrival—he is beneath your window.

This may not be exactly the picture you saw in your mind's eye as you read the verse. Everybody is affected somewhat differently. These differences in interpretation are part of what makes poetry so fascinating. Notice how the poet used many images to stir your feelings: "torrent of darkness," "gusty trees," "ghostly galleon," "cloudy seas," and "ribbon of moonlight." These colorful phrases kindle your imagination and prompt you to add more images of your own. Because much of this imagination springs from your own personality as well as from the poet's, your interpretation will vary slightly from other people's. It is probable that you did not picture the rider in the same manner as in the description following the poem. There is likely to be agreement among most readers, however, on one point: the scene pictured by the poet is sharp and vivid enough to create a special mood or atmosphere for each reader or listener. You must surely see, too, that Alfred Noyes has suggested a great deal with a few words, much more than you might expect from six short lines.

The effect of the next poem also depends heavily on your using your imagination, for you must feel the atmosphere of the scene described if the poem is to be meaningful. You know what *atmosphere* is; you are surely aware of the happy feeling that surrounds a joyous occasion—a dance, for example, or a victory celebration. At another time, perhaps when a death has occurred, the atmosphere or mood at a gathering is vastly different. Sometimes as you open a door and step into a room, you can almost sense the mood of the people within; silence or a significant glance from someone tells you how you must act. In this poem, try to feel the atmosphere that the Traveller sensed as he waited in the courtyard of an old deserted mansion.

THE LISTENERS

"Is there anybody there?" said the Traveller,
    Knocking on the moonlit door;
And his horse in the silence champed the grasses
    Of the forest's ferny floor.
And a bird flew up out of the turret,
    Above the Traveller's head:
And he smote upon the door again a second time;
    "Is there anybody there?" he said.
But no one descended to the Traveller;

No head from the leaf-fringed sill
Leaned over and looked into his gray eyes,
   Where he stood perplexed and still.
But only a host of phantom listeners
   That dwelt in the lone house then
Stood listening in the quiet of the moonlight
   To that voice from the world of men:
Stood thronging the faint moonbeams on the dark stair
   That goes down to the empty hall,
Hearkening in an air stirred and shaken
   By the lonely Traveller's call.
And he felt in his heart their strangeness,
   Their stillness answering his cry,
While his horse moved, cropping the dark turf,
   'Neath the starred and leafy sky;
For he suddenly smote on the door, even
   Louder, and lifted his head:
"Tell them I came, and no one answered,
   That I kept my word," he said.
Never the least stir made the listeners,
   Though every word he spake
Fell echoing through the shadowiness of the still house
   From the one man left awake:
Aye, they heard his foot upon the stirrup,
   And the sound of iron on stone,
And how the silence surged softly backward,
   When the plunging hoofs were gone.

             —WALTER DE LA MARE

   If you sensed the atmosphere of the old home, the poem begins to have meaning. You can picture the mansion itself, but who is the Traveller? Is he a knight? Has he returned from a mission of some kind? In what way and for what purpose has he kept his word?

More important than these questions, however, are the reasons that prompted him to raise his voice and speak to the apparently empty building. His actions seem at first hard to explain, but are they truly so strange? Have you ever driven past a deserted farmhouse and wondered who once lived there, and what happened to them? Have you ever turned to look behind you as you walked along a dark street at night, knowing no one was there but sensing a presence? Have you ever stepped across the crumbling old porch of an abandoned house, the planks creaking beneath your feet, and felt the need to knock on the door before entering? Did you feel a hesitation—a reluctance to intrude upon this scene? Your feeling was pure fantasy, for you knew there was no one within—or did you? Was there a powerful atmosphere surrounding the old ruins, one which seemed as real to you as the one that enveloped the Traveller in the poem? If you have ever had such a sensation, the poem speaks directly to you; the poet is describing almost the same emotion, using a setting alive with ghosts of the past. There are many such poems, for imagination and fantasy are completely at home in poetry.

Writers of poetry frequently make use of a technique that asks the reader to use both his imagination and his intellect. Many poets use *symbols* to give a deeper level of meaning to their works; that is, they use ideas that can mean two things at once. For example, here are some lines from a popular song of a few years ago:

> But it's a long, long while from May to December,
> And the days grow short when you reach September.

On the first level, the words seem to mean exactly what they say: it *is* a "long, long while from May to December," and it is equally true that the days do begin to "grow short" as autumn approaches. But if you think of a lifetime as a "year," you see immediately that there is another, deeper level of meaning: May becomes young adulthood; September is middle age; December is old age, followed by death. September represents that time when one's life is past its peak, when December seems so close—bringing with it the sharp realization of the approaching end. Thus the poet's use of symbols gives the poem two meanings: the obvious one is a graceful statement of fact; the secondary one is a commentary on the brevity of life.

It is perhaps now clear that the untrained reader who misses the symbolism of a poem can hardly grasp its full intent. Examine carefully these lines by Alfred, Lord Tennyson:

CROSSING THE BAR

Sunset and evening star,
> And one clear call for me!
And may there be no moaning of the bar,
> When I put out to sea,

But such a tide as moving seems asleep,
> Too full for sound and foam,
When that which drew from out the boundless deep
> Turns again home.

Twilight and evening bell,
> And after that the dark!
And may there be no sadness of farewell,
> When I embark;

For tho' from out our bourne of Time and Place
> The flood may bear me far,
I hope to see my Pilot face to face
> When I have crossed the bar.

—ALFRED, LORD TENNYSON

You may have understood both levels of meanings as you read. The first level may be interpreted something like this: the poet is speaking as one who is about to sail from a harbor at sunset. He wants it to be a joyful departure, one without "sadness" and hesitation. He speaks of meeting his "Pilot" when he has "crossed the bar"; that is, when he has cleared the harbor.

As you interpret the symbols, however, you find a far richer meaning. Tennyson is speaking not of a sea voyage, but of the voyage of death, which all must one day take. "Sunset" is the end of life; a "clear call" and a "tide . . . too full for sound or foam" refer to a life which ends without being painfully drawn out through illness or sorrow; the "Pilot" is God.

With the remarkable suggestive power that poetry has, moreover, the meaning of the poem is even greater than this. The writer is facing death unafraid and confident. Life has been a fine voyage; but the voyage after death will be even greater, for at the end of the journey there will be the ultimate experience of meeting his God, and the final mysteries of life will then be made clear. Tennyson asked before he died that this poem always be placed at the end of collections of his poetry, and the poem does indeed represent the tranquillity with which he faced life's close.

Another poem in which imagination and two levels of meaning are carefully interwoven is this one by William Butler Yeats:

WHEN YOU ARE OLD

When you are old and gray and full of sleep,
And nodding by the fire, take down this book,
And slowly read, and dream of the soft look
Your eyes had once, and of their shadows deep;

How many loved your moments of glad grace,
And loved your beauty with love false or true;
But one man loved the pilgrim soul in you,
And loved the sorrows of your changing face.

And bending down beside the glowing bars,
Murmur, a little sadly, how love fled
And paced upon the mountains overhead
And hid his face amid a crowd of stars.

—WILLIAM BUTLER YEATS

On the first level of meaning, you can see that the poet is suggesting to a woman he loves how she may find comfort in her old age. He urges her to remember the past when she was young and beautiful, and he advises her that these memories will bring consolation to her when she is "full of sleep."

When you give your imagination full play, however, you see that the fine images and poetic language tell also of a deep, tender love—a second level of meaning. The poet is apparently a successful writer, for he appears certain that his poem will be in "this book." You learn, further, that he loved her deeply and truly. There were "many," he tells her, who loved her with love "false and true," but his love for her extended beyond her beauty alone, since he loved her "pilgrim soul" and the "sorrows" of her "changing face." Last, you learn that "love fled" and "hid his face amid a crowd of stars." You realize now that he felt she would outlive him, and he was writing the poem as a memorial to her before his death. (He succeeded in this purpose; you have just read the memorial.) He does not despair at his approaching death and simply asks that she recall him fondly in her old age. Still, you cannot help feeling the overpowering love he must have had.

If you desire, you can go further than this, too, in what you let the poem say to you. There are many questions that you may consider. Was he older than she, that he expected to die before she did? Were they husband and wife? Was she a famous beauty, loved by many? What were the qualities of her "pilgrim soul"? What were the "sorrows" of her "changing face"? On and on the road of imagination may go. One short poem has opened a whole world to the mind and heart of the careful reader.

Sara Teasdale, a noted American poet, could also furnish these moments of wonder with her writing. Try to imagine all the levels of meaning she suggests as you read the next poem:

THE LONG HILL

I must have passed the crest a while ago
    And now I am going down—
Strange to have crossed the crest and not to know,
    But the brambles were always catching the hem of my gown.

All the morning I thought how proud I should be
    To stand there straight as a queen,
Wrapped in the wind and the sun with the world under me—
    But the air was dull, there was little I could have seen.

It was nearly level along the beaten track
    And the brambles caught in my gown—
But it's no use now to think of turning back,
    The rest of the way will be only going down.

                                              —SARA TEASDALE

There is much to think about in this poem. You can see rather
easily that here again are two levels. In the first, the writer, who has
climbed a "long hill," realizes she has passed the crest and is now
"going down." She tells you that she had hoped to be aware when
she was at the top, but that it was "nearly level," and she was so busy
with "brambles" that she hardly noticed the summit. That she had
missed this rewarding moment is a disappointment to her, for she
had planned, early in the morning as she began her climb, to pause
and breathe the fresh air when she reached the top. Now she has
already started down, and the opportunity will not come again. It is
too late to go back for another look.

You have probably guessed the second level of meaning. Life itself
is the "long hill," and the poet has passed the maturity of young
womanhood—the top of the hill—and is now moving past her
middle years toward old age—down the other side. The "brambles"
were the struggles and problems of life; she did not recognize the
magic moment when she arrived at womanhood; she passed it

without realizing it. Then, too, the expectation that life would be great and good on top of the hill was not fulfilled; she went along a "beaten track," one many others had followed, and the fine dreams and ambitions of her youth were not attained. She had expected success and contentment, but her troubles—the "brambles"—distracted her attention from the enjoyment of her mature period. As life is nearing its close, there is no way to recapture that lost youth. It is too late to turn back, and it is impossible anyway.

Another poet who wondered about the accomplishments of life was Percy Shelley. By now you are getting used to finding inner meanings in poems. Read this next one with attention to the poet's skill in telling two stories at the same time:

OZYMANDIAS

>I met a traveller from an antique land
>Who said: Two vast and trunkless legs of stone
>Stand in the desert . . . Near them, on the sand,
>Half sunk, a shattered visage lies, whose frown,
>And wrinkled lip, and sneer of cold command,
>Tell that its sculptor well those passions read
>Which yet survive, stamped on these lifeless things,
>The hand that mocked them and the heart that fed:
>And on the pedestal these words appear:
>"My name is Ozymandias, king of kings:
>Look on my works, ye Mighty, and despair!"
>Nothing beside remains. Round the decay
>Of that colossal wreck, boundless and bare
>The lone and level sands stretch far away.

>—PERCY BYSSHE SHELLEY

This poem is considered by many readers to be one of the finest in the English language. On the surface it tells a simple story. A traveller in an antique—that is, ancient—land came upon a broken statue in the desert. The statue was in pieces, with the face—"the shattered visage"—in one place, the legs in another. On the pedestal was the inscription composed by the man who had had the statue erected in his honor, "Ozymandias, king of kings." The face was regal, with a "sneer of cold command." The desert of "lone and level sands" was all that surrounded it. At first glance, there seems to be no great wisdom, no vivid picture, no word-music in the poem. Why, then, should it have such a reputation for excellence?

Perhaps you have now guessed the deeper meaning of the poem and the reason for its place in fine literature. Had it not been for the traveller who by purest chance happened to find the broken statue in the desert, you, the modern reader, would never have heard of this king with the curious name. Yet the boastful inscription reads: "Look on my works, ye mighty, and despair!" The proud king was certain that his great works would last forever, that his name would always be remembered and honored. The deeper truth of the poem thus becomes clear: no matter how famous your name and accomplishments may appear to be at the moment, you should not become vain, for in the vast expanse of time, the most magnificent names and events will be as meaningless as the ruined statue among the "lone and level sands."

POINTS TO REMEMBER

This chapter has presented several different poems, some that are easily interpreted, some that are understood only after a sincere effort to visualize the poet's purpose. The interpretations may vary slightly from those you might have given, or, for that matter, from the exact ideas the poet intended to convey. There will rarely be precise agreement as to what a poem means, for words are always subject to the various thoughts and beliefs of each reader. It does seem necessary, however, for you to develop certain special habits if you wish to enjoy and understand poetry fully:

Use your imagination. The poet, writing primarily to please himself, is not going to tell you his thoughts so fully as, for example, a short story writer might. If you are to appreciate the poem, you must be willing to think, to explore, and to dream.

Watch for the deeper meanings. The poet often is not content to put down his thoughts exactly as they come to him. He enriches them with the poet's picturesque language and imaginative constructions: images, similes, metaphors, and personifications. While your part in reading a poem should be primarily to enjoy, you will be rewarded if you look for these carefully planned levels of meaning that add depth. Interpreting the poet's symbols correctly will permit you to enlarge and enrich your understanding.

Read the poem several times. As you become familiar with a poem, your understanding of the poet's meaning generally increases. Remember, too, that you will be interpreting the poem through your own background and experiences; your responses may not be precisely what the poet had in mind. It is enough, however, to come close.

Read the poem aloud. The original purpose of poetry, you will recall, was to entertain listeners through a vocal presentation. This basic purpose is still unchanged, and the added enjoyment and understanding that come through oral reading make it a vital step in appreciating the full beauty of fine poetry.

CHAPTER THREE

Story Poems

The early English poets, as you have already learned, wrote exciting tales of heroes, monsters, and conflict. It is not surprising that story poems have continued to be popular all through the centuries, right down to the present day. As the years have gone by, many famous poets have written in the "narrative" style, telling stories of heroism in battle, tales of the sea, of pioneering, of love, of the sports world—anything that made a good story. Some of the poems are serious; others are humorous, even nonsensical. Many are based on actual happenings; still others are purely fictional, invented by the authors simply to amuse themselves and the readers. The result is a large number of poems that provide excitement and enjoyment.

In this section, you will find examples of several types of story poems, ranging all the way from a serious and stirring account of a famous battle ("The Charge of the Light Brigade") to the most fantastic nonsense ("The Two Old Bachelors"). They have all given pleasure to countless readers through the years. You will probably find some old friends among them; perhaps you will meet some new ones.

One of the best known of all story poems is the famous "Casey at the Bat." Many adults have known it all their lives and can quote whole sections of it from memory, particularly the final stanza. Almost everyone knows the ending, and yet the poem is read and re-read again and again, each time with more enjoyment.

CASEY AT THE BAT

It looked extremely rocky for the Mudville nine that day;
The score stood two to four, with but one inning left to play.
So, when Cooney died at second, and Burrows did the same,
A pallor wreathed the features of the patrons of the game.

A straggling few got up to go, leaving there the rest,
With that hope which springs eternal within the human breast.

For they thought: "If only Casey could get a whack at that,"
They'd put even money now, with Casey at the bat.

But Flynn preceded Casey, and likewise so did Blake,
And the former was a pudd'n, and the latter was a fake.
So on that stricken multitude a deathlike silence sat;
For there seemed but little chance of Casey's getting to the bat.

But Flynn let drive a "single," to the wonderment of all.
And the much-despisèd Blakey "tore the cover off the ball."
And when the dust had lifted, and they saw what had occurred,
There was Blakey safe at second, and Flynn a-huggin' third.

Then from the gladdened multitude went up a joyous yell—
It rumbled in the mountaintops, it rattled in the dell;
It struck upon the hillside and rebounded on the flat;
For Casey, mighty Casey, was advancing to the bat.

There was ease in Casey's manner as he stepped into his place,
There was pride in Casey's bearing and a smile on Casey's face;
And when responding to the cheers he lightly doffed his hat,
No stranger in the crowd could doubt 'twas Casey at the bat.

Ten thousand eyes were on him as he rubbed his hands with dirt.
Five thousand tongues applauded when he wiped them on his shirt;
Then when the writhing pitcher ground the ball into his hip,
Defiance glanced in Casey's eye, a sneer curled Casey's lip.

And now the leather-covered sphere came hurtling through the air,
And Casey stood a-watching it in haughty grandeur there.
Closeby the sturdy batsman the ball unheeded sped;
"That ain't my style," said Casey. "Strike one," the umpire said.

From the benches, black with people, there went up a muffled roar,
Like the beating of the storm waves on the stern and distant shore.
"Kill him! kill the umpire!" shouted someone on the stand;
And it's likely they'd have killed him had not Casey raised his hand.

With a smile of Christian charity great Casey's visage shone;
He stilled the rising tumult, he made the game go on;
He signaled to the pitcher, and once more the spheroid flew;
But Casey still ignored it, and the umpire said, "Strike two."

"Fraud!" cried the maddened thousands, and the echo answered "Fraud!"
But one scornful look from Casey and the audience was awed;
They saw his face grow stern and cold, they saw his muscles strain,
And they knew that Casey wouldn't let the ball go by again.

The sneer is gone from Casey's lips, his teeth are clenched in hate,
He pounds with cruel vengeance his bat upon the plate;
And now the pitcher holds the ball, and now he lets it go,
And now the air is shattered by the force of Casey's blow.

Oh, somewhere in this favored land the sun is shining bright,
The band is playing somewhere, and somewhere hearts are light;
And somewhere men are laughing, and somewhere children shout,
But there is no joy in Mudville—Mighty Casey has struck out.

—ERNEST LAWRENCE THAYER

Sometimes writers let the characters in their poems tell the tales in
their own colorful language. It may not always be "good" English,
but it gives a flavor to the stories that makes them seem very real.
Such a poem is "Jim Bludso, of the Prairie Belle," a story of the early
days of steam-boating on the Mississippi.

JIM BLUDSO
OF THE PRAIRIE BELLE

Wall, no! I can't tell whar he lives,
  Because he don't live, you see;
Leastways, he's got out of the habit
  Of livin' like you and me.

Whar have you been for the last three year
   That you haven't heard folks tell
How Jimmy Bludso passed in his checks
   The night of the Prairie Belle?

He warn't no saint,—them engineers
   Is all pretty much alike,—
One wife in Natchez-under-the-Hill
   And another one here, in Pike;
A keerless man in his talk was Jim,
   And an awkward hand in a row,
But he never flunked, and he never lied,—
   I reckon he never knowed how.

And this was all the religion he had,—
   To treat his engine well;
Never be passed on the river;
   To mind the pilot's bell;
And if ever the Prairie Belle took fire,—
   A thousand times he swore
He'd hold her nozzle agin the bank
   Till the last soul got ashore.

All boats has their day on the Mississip,
   And her day come at last,—
The Movastar was a better boat,
   But the Belle she *wouldn't* be passed.
And so she came tearin' along that night—
   The oldest craft on the line—
With a man a-squat on her safety valve,
   And her furnace crammed, rosin and pine.

The fire bust out as she clared the bar,
   And burnt a hole in the night,

And quick as a flash she turned, and made
    For that willer-bank on the right.
Thar was runnin' and cursin', but Jim yelled out,
    Over all the infernal roar,
"I'll hold her nozzle agin the bank
    Till the last galoot's ashore."

Through the hot, black breath of the burnin' boat
    Jim Bludso's voice was heard,
And they all had trust in his cussedness,
    And knowed he would keep his word.
And, sure's you're born, they all got off
    Afore the smokestacks fell,—
And Bludso's ghost went up alone
    In the smoke of the Prairie Belle.

He warn't no saint,—but at jedgment
    I'd run my chance with Jim,
'Longside of some pious gentlemen
    That wouldn't shook hands with him.
He seen his duty, a dead-sure thing,—
    And went for it thar and then;
And Christ ain't a-goin' to be too hard
    On a man that died for men.

—JOHN HAY

Nonsense verse is very hard to write. One of the best of the
nonsense poets is Edward Lear, who wrote many years ago. He has
built the following poem around a "pun"; that is, he uses a particular
word deliberately to mean two quite different things. Puns are usually
employed for humorous effect, as in this poem in which "sage"
means both a wise, learned man and an herb used for seasoning. The
real fun here, however, is largely in the clever rhyming, the lilting
meter, and the fanciful nonsense of the whole story.

THE TWO OLD BACHELORS

Two old Bachelors were living in one house;
One caught a Muffin, the other caught a Mouse.
Said he who caught the Muffin to him who caught the Mouse,—
"This happens just in time, for we've nothing in the house,
Save a tiny slice of lemon and a teaspoonful of honey,
And what to do for dinner,—since we haven't any money?
And what can we expect if we haven't any dinner
But to lose our teeth and eyelashes and keep on growing thinner?"

Said he who caught the Mouse to him who caught the Muffin,—
"We might cook this little Mouse if we only had some Stuffin'!
If we had but Sage and Onions we could do extremely well,
But how to get that Stuffin' it is difficult to tell!"—

And then those two old Bachelors ran quickly to the town
And asked for Sage and Onions as they wandered up and down;
They borrowed two large Onions, but no Sage was to be found
In the Shops or in the Market or in all the Gardens round.

But some one said, "A hill there is, a little to the north,
And to its purpledicular top a narrow way leads forth;
And there among the rugged rocks abides an ancient Sage,—
An earnest Man, who reads all day a most perplexing page.
Climb up and seize him by the toes,—all studious as he sits,—
And pull him down, and chop him into endless little bits!
Then mix him with your Onion (cut up likewise into scraps),
And your Stuffin' will be ready, and very good—perhaps."

And then those two old Bachelors, without loss of time,
The nearly purpledicular crags at once began to climb;
And at the top among the rocks, all seated in a nook,
They saw that Sage a-reading of a most enormous book.
"You earnest Sage!" aloud they cried, "your book you've read
    enough in!
We wish to chop you into bits and mix you into Stuffin'!"

But that old Sage looked calmly up, and with his awful book
At those two Bachelors' bald heads a certain aim he took;
And over crag and precipice they rolled promiscuous down,—
At once they rolled, and never stopped in lane or field or town;
And when they reached their house, they found (besides their want
   of Stuffin')
The Mouse had fled—and previously had eaten up the Muffin.

They left their home in silence by the once convivial door;
And from that hour those Bachelors were never heard of more.

—EDWARD LEAR

"The Cremation of Sam McGee," an imaginative tale of the gold-rush days in Alaska, is without a doubt one of the best-loved story poems in English. It can be re-read many times, and the enjoyment will be as great at later readings as it is with the first.

THE CREMATION OF SAM McGEE

There are strange things done in the midnight sun
By the men who moil for gold;
The Arctic trails have their secret tales
That would make your blood run cold;
The Northern Lights have seen queer sights,
But the queerest they ever did see
Was that night on the marge of Lake Lebarge
        I cremated Sam McGee.

Now Sam McGee was from Tennessee, where the cotton blooms and
   blows.
Why he left his home in the South to roam 'round the Pole, God
   only knows.
He was always cold, but the land of gold seemed to hold him like a
   spell;
Though he'd often say in his homely way that "he'd sooner live in
   hell."

On a Christmas Day we were mushing our way over the Dawson trail.

Talk of your cold! through the parka's fold it stabbed like a driven nail.

If our eyes we'd close, then the lashes froze till sometimes we couldn't see;

It wasn't much fun, but the only one to whimper was Sam McGee.

And that very night, as we lay packed tight in our robes beneath the snow,

And the dogs were fed, and the stars o'erhead were dancing heel and toe,

He turned to me, and "Cap," says he, "I'll cash in this trip, I guess;

And if I do, I'm asking that you won't refuse my last request."

Well, he seemed so low that I couldn't say no; then he says with a sort of moan:

"It's the cursed cold, and it's got right hold till I'm chilled clean through to the bone.

Yet 'tain't being dead—it's my awful dread of the icy grave that pains;

So I want you to swear that, foul or fair, you'll cremate my last remains."

A pal's last need is a thing to heed, so I swore I would not fail;

And we started on at the streak of dawn; but God! he looked ghastly pale.

He crouched on the sleigh, and he raved all day of his home in Tennessee;

And before nightfall a corpse was all that was left of Sam McGee.

There wasn't a breath in that land of death, and I hurried, horror-driven,

With a corpse half hid that I couldn't get rid, because of a promise given;

It was lashed to the sleigh, and it seemed to say: "You may tax your brawn and brains,
But you promised true, and it's up to you to cremate those last remains."

Now a promise made is a debt unpaid, and the trail has its own stern code.
In the days to come, though my lips were dumb, in my heart how I cursed that load.
In the long, long night, by the lone firelight, while the huskies, round in a ring,
Howled out their woes to the homeless snows—O God! how I loathed the thing.

And every day that quiet clay seemed to heavy and heavier grow;
And on I went, though the dogs were spent and the grub was getting low;
The trail was bad, and I felt half mad, but I swore I would not give in;
And I'd often sing to the hateful thing, and it hearkened with a grin.

Till I came to the marge of Lake Lebarge, and a derelict there lay;
It was jammed in the ice, but I saw in a trice it was called the "Alice May."
And I looked at it, and I thought a bit, and I looked at my frozen chum;
Then "Here," said I, with a sudden cry, "is my cre-ma-tor-eum."

Some planks I tore from the cabin floor, and I lit the boiler fire;
Some coal I found that was lying around, and I heaped the fuel higher;
The flames just soared, and the furnace roared—such a blaze you seldom see;
And I burrowed a hole in the glowing coal, and I stuffed in Sam McGee.

Then I made a hike, for I didn't like to hear him sizzle so;
And the heavens scowled, and the huskies howled, and the wind
    began to blow.
It was icy cold, but the hot sweat rolled down my cheeks, and I don't
    know why;
And the greasy smoke in an inky cloak went streaking down the sky.

I do not know how long in the snow I wrestled with grisly fear;
But the stars came out and they danced about ere again I ventured
    near;
I was sick with dread, but I bravely said: "I'll just take a peep inside.
I guess he's cooked, and it's time I looked"; . . . then the door I
    opened wide.

And there sat Sam, looking cold and calm, in the heart of the furnace
    roar;
And he wore a smile you could see a mile, and he said: "Please close
    that door.
It's fine in here, but I greatly fear you'll let in the cold and storm—
Since I left Plumtree, down in Tennessee, it's the first time I've been
    warm."

There are strange things done in the midnight sun
By the men who moil for gold;
The Arctic trails have their secret tales
That would make your blood run cold;
The Northern Lights have seen queer sights,
But the queerest they ever did see
Was that night on the marge of Lake Lebarge
        I cremated Sam McGee.

—ROBERT W. SERVICE

The story poems so far have all been rather light in tone. Often serious events are related in narrative verse, one of the most famous examples being Tennyson's "The Charge of the Light Brigade." He describes a thrilling cavalry battle of the last century. You may sense as you read it that while the poet is telling his story he is also making a very important point about war in general.

THE CHARGE OF THE LIGHT BRIGADE

Half a league, half a league,
Half a league, onward,
All in the valley of Death
   Rode the six hundred.
"Forward, the Light Brigade!
Charge for the guns!" he said.
Into the valley of Death
   Rode the six hundred.

"Forward, the Light Brigade!"
Was there a man dismayed?
Not though the soldier knew
   Someone had blundered.
Theirs not to make reply,
Theirs not to reason why,
Theirs but to do and die.
Into the valley of Death
   Rode the six hundred.

Cannon to right of them,
Cannon to left of them,
Cannon in front of them
   Volleyed and thundered;
Stormed at with shot and shell,
Boldly they rode and well
Into the jaws of Death,

Into the mouth of hell
  Rode the six hundred.

Flashed all their sabres bare,
Flashed as they turned in air
Sabring the gunners there,
Charging an army, while
  All the world wondered.
Plunged in the battery smoke
Right through the line they broke;
Cossack and Russian
Reeled from the sabre stroke
  Shattered and sundered.
Then they rode back, but not,
  Not the six hundred.

Cannon to right of them,
Cannon to left of them,
Cannon behind them
  Volleyed and thundered;
Stormed at with shot and shell,
While horse and hero fell,
They that had fought so well
Came through the jaws of Death,
Back from the mouth of hell,
All that was left of them,
  Left of six hundred.

When can their glory fade?
O the wild charge they made!
  All the world wondered.
Honor the charge they made!
Honor the Light Brigade,
  Noble six hundred!

—ALFRED, LORD TENNYSON

Another great war poem is Kipling's "Gunga Din." As in "Jim Bludso" and "The Cremation of Sam McGee," it is written in the rather ungrammatical, colorful speech of a soldier who is a part of the story. This time, however, the language is that of a member of the British Colonial Army in India many years ago before India became an independent nation. You will find a number of expressions for which you will need to use the notes following the poem. The story is nevertheless clear, the message plain, and several of the phrases used have become a part of our everyday speech.

GUNGA DIN

You may talk o' gin an' beer
When you're quartered safe out 'ere,
An' you're sent to penny-fights an' Aldershot it;
But when it comes to slaughter
You will do your work on water,
An' you'll lick the bloomin' boots of 'im that's got it.
Now in Injia's sunny clime,
Wher I used to spend my time
A-servin' of 'Er Majesty the Queen,
Of all them black-faced crew
The finest man I knew
Was our regimental bhisti, Gunga Din.

He was "Din! Din! Din!
You limpin' lump o' brick-dust, Gunga Din!
Hi! slippy *hitherao!*
Water, get it! *Panee lao!*
You squidgy-nosed old idol, Gunga Din!"

The uniform 'e wore
Was nothin' much before,
An' rather less than 'arf o' that be'ind,

For a piece o' twisty rag
An' a goatskin water-bag
Was all the field-equipment 'e could find.
When the sweatin' troop-train lay
In a sidin' through the day,
Where the 'eat would make your bloomin' eyebrows crawl,
We shouted *"Harry By!"*
Till our throats were bricky-dry,
Then we wopped 'im 'cause 'e couldn't serve us all.

> It was "Din! Din! Din!
> You 'eathen, where the mischief 'ave you been?
> You put some *juldee* in it,
> Or I'll *marrow* you this minute,
> If you don't fill up my helmet, Gunga Din!"

'E would dot an' carry one
Till the longest day was done,
An' 'e didn't seem to know the use o' fear.
If we charged or broke or cut,
You could bet your bloomin' nut,
'E'd be waitin' fifty paces right flank rear.
With 'is mussick on 'is back,
'E would skip with our attack,
An' watch us till the bugles made "Retire."
An' for all 'is dirty 'ide,
'E was white, clear white, inside
When 'e went to tend the wounded under fire!

> It was "Din! Din! Din!
> With the bullets kickin' dust-spots on the green.
> When the cartridges ran out,
> You could 'ear the front-ranks shout,
> "Hi! ammunition-mules an' Gunga Din!"

I shan't forgit the night
When I dropped be'ind the fight
With a bullet where my belt-plate should 'a' been.
I was chokin' mad with thirst,
An' the man that spied me first
Was our good old grinnin', gruntin' Gunga Din.
'E lifted up my 'ead,
An' he plugged me where I bled,
An' 'e guv me 'arf-a-pint o' water green.
It was crawlin' and it stunk,
But of all the drinks I've drunk,
I'm gratefullest to one from Gunga Din.

It was "Din! Din! Din!
'Ere's a beggar with a bullet through 'is spleen;
'E's chawin' up the ground
An' 'e's kickin' all around:
For Gawd's sake, git the water, Gunga Din!"

'E carried me away
To where a dooli lay,
An' a bullet come an' drilled the beggar clean.
'E put me safe inside,
An' just before 'e died:
"I 'ope you liked your drink," sez Gunga Din.
So I'll meet 'im later on
In the place where 'e is gone—
Where it's always double drill and no canteen.
'E'll be squattin' on the coals
Givin' drink to pore damned souls,
An' I'll get a swig in Hell from Gunga Din!

Yes, Din! Din! Din!
You Lazarushian-leather Gunga Din!
    Though I've belted you and flayed you,
    By the livin' Gawd that made you,
You're a better man than I am, Gunga Din!

—RUDYARD KIPLING

---

bhisti, native water carrier   *slippy hitherao,* make it snappy
Panee lao, bring that water fast
Harry By, an exclamation of mild despair
juldee, speed   *marrow,* hit   *mussick,* water canteen
dooli, stretcher

Story poems are well suited to accounts of heroism as in "Gunga Din." They are equally at home with tales of young love, as the next poem will show. The scene is romantic Scotland, many hundreds of years ago when knighthood was in flower. Being a knight was no guarantee that the course of true love would run smoothly, however, and this young man had to take extreme measures to win his lady love.

YOUNG LOCHINVAR

Oh, young Lochinvar is come out of the west,
Through all the wide Border his steed was the best;
And, save his good broadsword, he weapon had none,
He rode all unarmed, and he rode all alone.
So faithful in love, and so dauntless in war,
There never was knight like the young Lochinvar.

He stayed not for brake, and he stopped not for stone,
He swam the Eske River where ford there was none;

But, ere he alighted at Netherby gate,
The bride had consented, the gallant came late;
For a laggard in love, and a dastard in war,
Was to wed the fair Ellen of brave Lochinvar.

So boldly he entered the Netherby Hall,
Among bridesmen, and kinsmen, and brothers, and all.
Then spoke the bride's father, his hand on his sword,
(For the poor craven bridegroom said never a word),
"Oh, come ye in peace here, or come ye in war,
Or to dance at our bridal, young Lord Lochinvar?"

"I long wooed your daughter, my suit you denied;—
Love swells like the Solway, but ebbs like its tide,—
And now am I come, with this lost love of mine,
To lead but one measure, drink one cup of wine,
There are maidens in Scotland more lovely by far,
That would gladly be bride to the young Lochinvar."

The bride kissed the goblet; the knight took it up,
He quaffed off the wine, and he threw down the cup.
She looked down to blush, and she looked up to sigh,
With a smile on her lips, and a tear in her eye.
He took her soft hand, ere her mother could bar,—
"Now tread we a measure!" said young Lochinvar.

So stately his form, and so lovely her face,
That never a hall such a galliard did grace;
While her mother did fret, and her father did fume,
And the bridegroom stood dangling his bonnet and plume;
And the bride-maidens whispered, "'Twere better by far
To have matched our fair cousin with young Lochinvar."

One touch to her hand, and one word in her ear,
When they reached the hall-door, and the charger stood near:
So light to the croupe the fair lady he swung,
So light to the saddle before her he sprung!

"She is won! we are gone! over bank, bush, and scaur;
They'll have fleet steeds that follow," quoth young Lochinvar.

There was mounting 'mong Graemes of the Netherby clan;
Forsters, Fenwicks, and Musgraves, they rode and they ran:
There was racing and chasing on Canobie Lee,
But the lost bride of Netherby ne'er did they see.
So daring in love, and so dauntless in war,
Have ye e'er heard of gallant like young Lochinvar?

—SIR WALTER SCOTT

Young love may be thrilling, as in "Lochinvar"; it may also be
tragic, ending in death for one of the lovers. Most people have
serious moments when they wonder about the mystery of death, and
the poets often are concerned with it in their writings. Sometimes
they see death as a tragic conclusion to life, sometimes as the beginning of a great adventure, sometimes as an unsolved puzzle. The
following poem by Edgar Allan Poe speaks of the death of his own
wife, a girl he had married at a very young age, and who died of
tuberculosis before she was twenty.

ANNABEL LEE

It was many and many a year ago,
        In a kingdom by the sea,
That a maiden there lived whom you may know
        By the name of ANNABEL LEE;
And this maiden she lived with no other thought
        Than to love and be loved by me.

I was a child and she was a child,
        In this kingdom by the sea,
But we loved with a love that was more than love—
        I and my ANNABEL LEE—
With a love that wingèd seraphs of heaven
        Coveted her and me.

And this was the reason that, long ago,
  In this kingdom by the sea,
A wind blew out of a cloud, chilling
  My beautiful ANNABEL LEE,
So that her high-born kinsmen came
  And bore her away from me,
To shut her up in a sepulchre
  In this kingdom by the sea.

The angels, not half so happy in heaven,
  Went envying her and me—
Yes!—that was the reason (as all men know,
  In this kingdom by the sea)
That the wind came out of the cloud by night,
  Chilling and killing my ANNABEL LEE.

But our love it was stronger by far than the love
  Of those who were older than we—
  Of many far wiser than we—
And neither the angels in heaven above,
  Nor the demons down under the sea,
Can ever dissever my soul from the soul
  Of the beautiful ANNABEL LEE:

For the moon never beams, without bringing me dreams
  Of the beautiful ANNABEL LEE:
And the stars never rise, but I feel the bright eyes
  Of the beautiful ANNABEL LEE:
And so, all the night-tide, I lie down by the side
Of my darling—my darling—my life and my bride,
  In the sepulchre there by the sea—
  In her tomb by the sounding sea.

—EDGAR ALLAN POE

When death strikes, it often touches those who seem the least likely to be chosen. Annabel Lee, in her youth and beauty, was such a person. Richard Cory, in the next poem, is another, although for different reasons.

RICHARD CORY

Whenever Richard Cory went down town,
    We people on the pavement looked at him:
He was a gentleman from sole to crown,
    Clean favored, and imperially slim.

And he was always quietly arrayed,
    And he was always human when he talked;
But still he fluttered pulses when he said,
    "Good-morning," and he glittered when he walked.

And he was rich—yes, richer than a king—
    And admirably schooled in every grace:
In fine, we thought that he was everything
    To make us wish that we were in his place.

So on we worked, and waited for the light,
    And went without the meat, and cursed the bread;
And Richard Cory, one calm summer night,
    Went home and put a bullet through his head.

          —EDWIN ARLINGTON ROBINSON

One of America's best-loved poets was Robert Frost. In the next poem, once again the theme is death, but Frost develops the subject in a very different style from that of the previous two poems. You will notice also that the form is different—for one thing, there is no rhyme; for another, a large part of the poem is conversation. The dialogue between the two people is presented in a realistic way, and yet the choice of words and the natural rhythm of the language make this story just as poetic as that of "Annabel Lee" and "Richard Cory."

THE DEATH OF THE HIRED MAN

Mary sat musing on the lamp-flame at the table
Waiting for Warren. When she heard his step,
She ran on tip-toe down the darkened passage
To meet him in the doorway with the news
And put him on his guard. "Silas is back."
She pushed him outward with her through the door
And shut it after her. "Be kind," she said.
She took the market things from Warren's arms
And set them on the porch, then drew him down
To sit beside her on the wooden steps.

"When was I ever anything but kind to him?
But I'll not have the fellow back," he said.
"I told him so last haying, didn't I?
'If he left then,' I said, 'that ended it.'
What good is he? Who else will harbor him
At his age for the little he can do?
What help he is there's no depending on.
Off he goes always when I need him most.
'He thinks he ought to earn a little pay,
Enough at least to buy tobacco with,
So he won't have to beg and be beholden.'
'All right,' I say, 'I can't afford to pay
Any fixed wages, though I wish I could.'
'Someone else can.' 'Then someone else will have to.'
I shouldn't mind his bettering himself
If that was what it was. You can be certain,

When he begins like that, there's someone at him
Trying to coax him off with pocket-money,—
In haying time, when any help is scarce.
In winter he comes back to us. I'm done."

"Sh! not so loud: he'll hear you," Mary said.

"I want him to: he'll have to soon or late."

"He's worn out. He's asleep beside the stove.
When I came up from Rowe's I found him here,
Huddled against the barn-door fast asleep,
A miserable sight, and frightening, too—
You needn't smile—I didn't recognize him—
I wasn't looking for him—and he's changed.
Wait till you see."

                              "Where did you say he'd been?"

"He didn't say. I dragged him to the house,
And gave him tea and tried to make him smoke.
I tried to make him talk about his travels.
Nothing would do: he just kept nodding off."

"What did he say? Did he say anything?"

"But little."

                    "Anything? Mary, confess
He said he'd come to ditch the meadow for me."

"Warren!"

              "But did he? I just want to know."

"Of course he did. What would you have him say?
Surely you wouldn't grudge the poor old man
Some humble way to save his self-respect.
He added, if you really care to know,
He meant to clear the upper pasture, too.

That sounds like something you have heard before?
Warren, I wish you could have heard the way
He jumbled everything. I stopped to look
Two or three times—he made me feel so queer—
To see if he was talking in his sleep.
He ran on Harold Wilson—you remember—
The boy you had in haying four years since.
He's finished school, and teaching in his college.
Silas declares you'll have to get him back.
He says they two will make a team for work:
Between them they will lay this farm as smooth!
The way he mixed that in with other things.
He thinks young Wilson a likely lad, though daft
On education—you know how they fought
All through July under the blazing sun,
Silas up on the cart to build the load,
Harold along beside to pitch it on."

"Yes, I took care to keep well out of earshot."

"Well, those days trouble Silas like a dream.
You wouldn't think they would. How some things linger!
Harold's young college boy's assurance piqued him.
After so many years he still keeps finding
Good arguments he sees he might have used.
I sympathize. I know just how it feels
To think of the right thing to say too late.
Harold's associated in his mind with Latin.
He asked me what I thought of Harold's saying
He studied Latin like the violin
Because he liked it—that an argument!
He said he couldn't make the boy believe
He could find water with a hazel prong—
Which showed how much good school had ever done him.

He wanted to go over that. But most of all
He thinks if he could have another chance
To teach him how to build a load of hay—"

"I know, that's Silas' one accomplishment.
He bundles every forkful in its place,
And tags and numbers it for future reference,
So he can find and easily dislodge it
In the unloading. Silas does that well.
He takes it out in bunches like big birds' nests.
You never see him standing on the hay
He's trying to lift, straining to lift himself."

"He thinks if he could teach him that, he'd be
Some good perhaps to someone in the world.
He hates to see a boy the fool of books.
Poor Silas, so concerned for other folk,
And nothing to look backward to with pride,
And nothing to look forward to with hope,
So now and never any different."

Part of a moon was falling down the west,
Dragging the whole sky with it to the hills.
Its light poured softly in her lap. She saw it
And spread her apron to it. She put out her hand
Among the harp-like morning-glory strings,
Taut with the dew from garden bed to eaves,
As if she played unheard some tenderness
That wrought on him beside her in the night.
"Warren," she said, "he has come home to die:
You needn't be afraid he'll leave you this time."

"Home," he mocked gently.

     "Yes, what else but home?
It all depends on what you mean by home.

Of course he's nothing to us, any more
Than was the hound that came a stranger to us
Out of the woods, worn out upon the trail."

"Home is the place where, when you have to go there,
They have to take you in."

                              "I should have called it
Something you somehow haven't to deserve."

Warren leaned out and took a step or two,
Picked up a little stick, and brought it back
And broke it in his hand and tossed it by.
"Silas has better claim on us, you think,
Than on his brother? Thirteen little miles
As the road winds would bring him to his door.
Silas has walked that far no doubt to-day.
Why didn't he go there? His brother's rich,
A somebody—director in the bank."

"He never told us that."

                        "We know it though."

"I think his brother ought to help, of course.
I'll see to that if there is need. He ought of right
To take him in, and might be willing to—
He may be better than appearances.
But have some pity on Silas. Do you think
If he'd had any pride in claiming kin
Or anything he looked for from his brother,
He'd keep so still about him all this time?"

"I wonder what's between them."

                           "I can tell you.
Silas is what he is—we wouldn't mind him—
But just the kind that kinsfolk can't abide.
He never did a thing so very bad.

He don't know why he isn't quite as good
As anyone. Worthless though he is,
He won't be made ashamed to please his brother."

"I can't think Si ever hurt anyone."

"No, but he hurt my heart the way he lay
And rolled his old head on that sharp-edged chair-back.
He wouldn't let me put him on the lounge.
You must go in and see what you can do.
I made the bed up for him there to-night.
You'll be surprised at him—how much he's broken.
His working days are done; I'm sure of it."

"I'd not be in a hurry to say that."

"I haven't been. Go, look, see for yourself.
But, Warren, please remember how it is:
He's come to help you ditch the meadow.
He has a plan. You mustn't laugh at him.
He may not speak of it, and then he may.
I'll sit and see if that small sailing cloud
Will hit or miss the moon."

                      It hit the moon.
Then there were three there, making a dim row,
The moon, the little silver cloud, and she.

Warren returned—too soon, it seemed to her,
Slipped to her side, caught up her hand and waited.

"Warren?" she questioned.

                "Dead," was all he answered.

—ROBERT FROST

1. In "Casey at the Bat" the author uses the unexpected to gain his humorous effect. Explain how this procedure contributes to the fun.

2. Why doesn't the poet of "Casey at the Bat" come directly to the point in the last stanza and tell you immediately that Casey struck out?

3. How would you describe Jim Bludso's "religion"? Explain how he was true to his beliefs.

4. What would have been the difference in the effect of this poem if the poet had used more "socially" correct English in telling the story of Jim Bludso?

5. What are some of the ideas in "The Two Old Bachelors" that make the poem nonsensical and fantastic?

6. Explain the play on words that is the basis for Edward Lear's poem and give two examples of other puns you may have heard.

7. "The Cremation of Sam McGee" is effective partly because of the strange story, partly because it uses "internal rhyme" (that is, rhyming words within the line as well as at the ends of lines). Point out some examples of this internal rhyme.

8. Why do you think Robert W. Service repeated the first stanza again at the end of the poem?

9. Soldiers sometimes quote these two lines from "The Charge of the Light Brigade":

> Theirs not to reason why,
> Theirs but to do or die.

In what ways does this summarize the attitude expected of a typical soldier in the service?

10. What strong point (never stated directly in the poem) does the poet of "The Charge of the Light Brigade" make concerning war in general?

11. An entire full-length film has been made which used the poem "Gunga Din" for the greater portion of its plot. In what ways would this poem serve as a basis for a good film story?

12. Give as many reasons as you can why the last line of "Gunga Din" ("You're a better man than I am, Gunga Din") is the very heart of the poem.

13. Why was young Lochinvar compelled to carry off his sweetheart as he did?

14. Often the meanings of words that are strange to you can be understood from the way they are used (from their "context"). In "Young Lochinvar," before looking up or asking the meanings of words that are new to you, see how many you can define through context. In what ways do certain unusual words contribute to the over-all effect of the poem?

15. In "Annabel Lee" how does the poet suggest the happiness of the marriage, brief and tragic though it was?

16. Edgar Allan Poe was a master of words. Look back over the poem and observe how he used a vocabulary of soft, liquid sounds. Notice how many words contain "l's," "m's," and "o's." Notice, too, how he chose his words and arranged them in such form as would produce a quiet but very definite rhythm of an almost musical nature. Many experienced readers refer to such poetry as being "music" in words. Point out specifically some of the words and phrases by which Poe achieved this musical effect.

17. What do you see in your mind's-eye when you think of Richard Cory's "glittering" when he walked? How does this word bring much more to mind than it actually means?

18. What basic point do you think the poet of "Richard Cory" is trying to convey to you?

19. In Robert Frost's poem "The Death of the Hired Man," Warren gives a definition of what home is. What do you think of this definition? How is it appropriate to the story told in this poem?

20. Many readers of Frost's poem find they are deeply moved at its ending; yet the poem does not preach a sermon or point heavily toward a moral. Why is it that the poet is able to achieve this stirring effect?

CHAPTER FOUR
Young People

You are in a period of your life that carries with it mixed blessings. It would seem a mistake to call it truly unhappy, for nearly all older people insist that the days of their youth were the happiest of their lives, and it seems unlikely that all these adults can be wrong. Their statements run something like this: young people do not need to worry about the responsibilities of earning a living and rearing a family; they are free to laugh, to dream, to enjoy themselves; never again will they be so carefree.

On the other hand, there seems to be something the matter with being young, for nearly all young people look forward eagerly to the day when they will leave this period of their lives and enter adulthood. Part of the trouble, perhaps, comes from the critical attitude of the older generation. They tend to glorify their own youthful years and to be impatient or to laugh at the "crazy teenagers" of today. Many old-timers have conveniently forgotten the problems (and often their own conduct) of their early period. This tendency to look back in time through rose-colored glasses has been common since the days of Plato, a famous Greek philosopher who, more than two thousand years ago, also was worried about the "younger generation."

More important to you than anything else, however, are the problems that concern you deeply at this point in your life. You wonder what kind of person you will become some day, what your life work will be, when you will stop daydreaming, how you may bring real meaning into your life, how you can get others to like you, how you can make your parents understand you. These are all serious problems, and you rightfully resent the attitudes of those older people who often seem to be unsympathetic toward you and your concerns.

Many of the finest poets have managed to remain young in heart. They often express in their poems an understanding of the youthful point of view and of the worries that trouble young people. The poems in this chapter will show you that most of your own doubts and concerns are not unique, but have been shared by others all through the years. There is a great deal of comfort in finding your problems appreciated by thoughtful people and expressed sympathetically in their writings.

The first poem in this group has to do with that favorite pastime of young people—daydreaming. Poets, who are dreamers themselves, or they wouldn't be poets, view this pleasant activity with great sympathy. Louise Driscoll's "Hold Fast Your Dreams!" gives a word of encouragement (and advice) to all young daydreamers.

HOLD FAST YOUR DREAMS!

Hold fast your dreams!
Within your heart
Keep one, still, secret spot
Where dreams may go,
And sheltered so,
May thrive and grow—
Where doubt and fear are not.
O keep a place apart,
Within your heart,
For little dreams to go!

Think still of lovely things that are not true.
Let wish and magic work at will in you.
Be sometimes blind to sorrow. Make believe!
Forget the calm that lies
In disillusioned eyes.
Though we all know that we must die,
Yet you and I
May walk like gods and be
Even now at home in immortality!

We see so many ugly things—
Deceits and wrongs and quarrelings;
We know, alas! we know
How quickly fade

The color in the west,
The bloom upon the flower,
The bloom upon the breast,
The youth's blind hour.
Yet, keep within your heart
A place apart
Where little dreams may go,
May thrive and grow.
Hold fast—hold fast your dreams!

—LOUISE DRISCOLL

You have probably heard it said that good children become good adults—that what you do as young people shapes your later lives. Now and then, however, one hears stories of the wild youth who develops into the model citizen. "You never can tell."

THOSE TWO BOYS

When Bill was a lad he was terribly bad.
    He worried his parents a lot;
He'd lie and he'd swear and pull little girls' hair;
    His boyhood was naught but a blot.

At play and in school he would fracture each rule—
    In mischief from autumn to spring;
And the villagers knew when to manhood he grew
    He would never amount to a thing.

When Jim was a child he was not very wild;
    He was known as a good little boy;
He was honest and bright and the teacher's delight—
    To his mother and father a joy.

All the neighbors were sure that his virtue'd endure,
    That his life would be free of a spot;
They were certain that Jim had a great head on him
    And that Jim would amount to a lot.

And Jim grew to manhood and honor and fame
    And bears a good name;
While Bill is shut up in a dark prison cell—
    You never can tell.

—FRANKLIN P. ADAMS

As you study history and learn of the great deeds and heroes of the past, you may sometimes wonder whether all the fine things have already been done, all the strange lands explored, all the wonderful happenings recorded. What is left for you to do? Berton Braley sums up your prospects in this way:

OPPORTUNITY

With doubt and dismay you are smitten;
    You think there's no chance for you, son?
Why, the best books haven't been written,
    The best race hasn't been run,
The best score hasn't been made yet,
    The best song hasn't been sung,
The best tune hasn't been played yet.
    Cheer up, for the world is young!

No chance? Why the world is just eager
    For things that you ought to create:
Its store of true wealth is still meager
    Its needs are incessant and great;

It yearns for more power and beauty,
  More laughter and love and romance,
More loyalty, labor and duty;
  No chance? Why, there's nothing but chance!

For the best verse hasn't been rhymed yet,
  The best house hasn't been planned,
The highest sky hasn't been climbed yet,
  The mightiest rivers aren't spanned.
Don't worry and fret, faint-hearted;
  The chances have just begun.
For the best jobs haven't been started—
  The best work hasn't been done!

—BERTON BRALEY

The "best work" may be yet to be done, but there are decisions that must be made before you begin this work. Perhaps the most important choice you will make will be what to do with your life—what direction to take—and you must make this decision before you have had much experience to guide you. Robert Frost, in the next poem, speaks of *his* moment of decision and its results.

THE ROAD NOT TAKEN

Two roads diverged in a yellow wood,
And sorry I could not travel both
And be one traveler, long I stood
And looked down one as far as I could
To where it bent in the undergrowth;

Then took the other, as just as fair,
And having perhaps the better claim,
Because it was grassy and wanted wear;
Though as for that the passing there
Had worn them really about the same,

And both that morning equally lay
In leaves no step had trodden black.
Oh, I kept the first for another day!
Yet knowing how way leads on to way,
I doubted if I should ever come back.

I shall be telling this with a sigh
Somewhere ages and ages hence:
Two roads diverged in a wood, and I—
I took the one less traveled by,
And that has made all the difference.

—ROBERT FROST

One of the most important words in the English language is the little word *if*. Rudyard Kipling uses it as the title and the basis of a famous poem. He speaks here of some of the important values in life that he believes must be understood by all young people who wish to become truly adult.

I F

If you can keep your head when all about you
    Are losing theirs and blaming it on you,
If you can trust yourself when all men doubt you,
    But make allowance for their doubting too;
If you can wait and not be tired by waiting,
    Or being lied about, don't deal in lies,
Or being hated, don't give way to hating,
    And yet don't look too good, nor talk too wise:

If you can dream—and not make dreams your master;
    If you can think—and not make thoughts your aim;
If you can meet with Triumph and Disaster
    And treat those two impostors just the same;

If you can bear to hear the truth you've spoken
      Twisted by knaves to make a trap for fools,
Or watch the things you gave your life to, broken,
      And stoop and build 'em up with worn-out tools:

If you can make one heap of all your winnings
      And risk it on one turn of pitch-and-toss,
And lose, and start again at your beginnings
      And never breathe a word about your loss;
If you can force your heart and nerve and sinew
      To serve your turn long after they are gone,
And so hold on when there is nothing in you
      Except the will which says to them: "Hold on!"

If you can talk with crowds and keep your virtue,
      Or walk with kings—nor lose the common touch,
If neither foes nor loving friends can hurt you,
      If all men count with you, but none too much;
If you can fill the unforgiving minute
      With sixty seconds' worth of distance run,
Yours is the earth and everything that's in it,
      And—which is more—you'll be a man, my son!

—RUDYARD KIPLING

Young people have one marvelous advantage over their elders—the chance to discover, as if they never were discovered before, the joys and beauties that life holds. Sara Teasdale understands the value of beautiful experiences—and she understands the cost.

BARTER

      Life has loveliness to sell,
          All beautiful and splendid things,
      Blue waves whitened on a cliff,
          Soaring fire that sways and sings,
      And children's faces looking up
      Holding wonder like a cup.

Life has loveliness to sell,
　　Music like a curve of gold,
Scent of pine trees in the rain,
　　Eyes that love you, arms that hold,
And for your spirit's still delight,
Holy thoughts that star the night.

Spend all you have for loveliness,
　　Buy it and never count the cost;
For one white singing hour of peace
　　Count many a year of strife well lost,
And for a breath of ecstasy
Give all you have been, or could be.

—SARA TEASDALE

The moments of loveliness that Sara Teasdale speaks of can make the problems of life seem less distressing. There is so much in the world that makes up for the daily worries of existence. Some fine morning when you rise and look out on a beautiful day, life may seem like this:

ADVENTURE

Sun and wind and beat of sea,
Great lands stretching endlessly . . .
Where be bonds to bind the free?
All the world was made for me!

—ADELAIDE CRAPSEY

With all of life lying ahead, and nature beckoning to you, it is little wonder that you may sometime have had this comment made about you: "He means well, but he just can't settle down to work." If you have ever been the victim of such a remark, you may recognize yourself as "I" in the next poem.

I MEANT TO DO MY WORK TODAY

I meant to do my work today—
>   But a brown bird sang in the apple-tree,
And a butterfly flitted across the field,
>   And all the leaves were calling me.

And the wind went sighing over the land,
>   Tossing the grasses to and fro,
And a rainbow held out its shining hand—
>   So what could I do but laugh and go?

—RICHARD LE GALLIENNE

It may not actually be butterflies or rainbows that call to you, but the specific things that Richard Le Gallienne mentions symbolize all the voices that speak to the heart of youth. To John Masefield it was the sea that called, and it summoned him so strongly that most of his life and writings were deeply concerned with its irresistible voice.

A WANDERER'S SONG

A wind's in the heart of me, a fire's in my heels,
I am tired of brick and stone and rumbling wagon-wheels;
I hunger for the sea's edge, the limits of the land,
Where the wild old Atlantic is shouting on the sand.

Oh I'll be going, leaving the noises of the street,
To where a lifting foresail-foot is yanking at the sheet;
To a windy, tossing anchorage where yawls and ketches ride,
Oh I'll be going, going, until I meet the tide.

And first I'll hear the sea-wind, the mewing of the gulls,
The clucking, sucking of the sea about the rusty hulls,
The songs at the capstan in the hooker warping out,
And then the heart of me'll know I'm there or thereabout.

Oh I am sick of brick and stone, the heart of me is sick,
For windy green, unquiet sea, the realm of Moby Dick;
And I'll be going, going, from the roaring of the wheels,
For a wind's in the heart of me, a fire's in my heels.

—JOHN MASEFIELD

Several of the poems in this chapter speak of the voices that summon the youth away from his immediate duties. You will hear this call all of your days, but it is never so loud as in the spring of life, when spring itself beckons you.

THE CALL OF THE SPRING

Come, choose your road and away, my lad,
    Come, choose your road and away!
We'll out of the town by the road's bright crown
    As it dips to the dazzling day.
It's a long white road for the weary;
    But it rolls through the heart of the May.

Though many a road would merrily ring
    To the tramp of your marching feet,
All roads are one from the day that's done,
    And the miles are swift and sweet,
And the graves of your friends are the mile-stones
    To the land where all roads meet.

But the call that you hear this day, my lad,
    Is the Spring's old bugle of mirth
When the year's green fire in a soul's desire
    Is brought like a rose to the birth:
And knights ride out to adventure
    As the flowers break out of the earth.

Over the sweet-smelling mountain-passes
    The clouds lie brightly curled;
The wild-flowers cling to the crags and swing
    With cataract-dews impearled;
And the way, the way that you choose this day
    Is the way to the end of the world.

It rolls from the golden long ago
    To the land that we ne'er shall find;
And it's uphill here, but it's downhill there,
    For the road is wise and kind,
And all rough places and cheerless faces
    Will soon be left behind.

Come, choose your road and away, away,
    We'll follow the gipsy sun;
For it's soon, too soon to the end of the day,
    And the day is well begun;
And the road rolls on through the end of the May,
    And there's never a May but one.

There's a fir-wood here, and a dog-rose there,
    And a note of the mating dove;
And a glimpse, maybe, of the warm blue sea,
    And the warm white clouds above;
And warm to your breast in a tenderer nest
    Your sweetheart's little glove.

There's not much better to win, my lad,
    There's not much better to win!
You have lived, you have loved, you have fought,
    You have proved the worth of folly and sin;
So now come out of the City's rout,
    Come out of the dust and din.

Come out,—a bundle and stick is all
    You'll need to carry along,
If your heart can carry a kindly word,
    And your lips can carry a song;
You may leave the lave to the keep o' the grave,
    If your lips can carry a song!

Come, choose your road and away, my lad,
    Come choose your road and away!
We'll out of the town by the road's bright crown,
    As it dips to the sapphire day!
All roads may meet at the world's end,
    But hey for the heart of the May!
Come, choose your road and away, dear lad,
    Come choose your road and away.

—ALFRED NOYES

You may have noticed that none of the fine poets you have read so far tells you exactly what to do to enjoy your youth and the years ahead. Rather, each suggests how to approach life—how to look at it so that your own unique responses will be the most rewarding. They leave it up to you to decide exactly what choices to make. Lizette Woodworth Reese has this same reluctance to tell you *what* to do, but she suggests a goal toward which you may work.

A LITTLE SONG OF LIFE

Glad that I live am I;
That the sky is blue;
Glad for the country lanes,
And the fall of dew.

After the sun the rain;
After the rain the sun;
This is the way of life,
Till work be done.

All that we need to do,
Be we low or high,
Is to see that we grow
Nearer the sky.

—LIZETTE WOODWORTH REESE

Growing "nearer the sky" is a lifelong process. At sixteen (or fifteen or fourteen) you are just beginning, and it often must seem difficult to get started. You are, however, remarkably alive. A poet of your own age has written of these years in this way:

SIXTEEN

Sixteen
sees and laughs,
listens and sighs,
sleeps and eats,
aches and cries,
babbles, thinks,
loves and hates,
stretches, lives
and hopefully waits.

—CAROLYN CAHALAN

One of the promises of life for which the girl of "Sixteen" is awaiting fulfillment is love. Young love is among the finest of all emotions, and love is probably the subject of more poems than any other single inspiration. The next three poems are examples of some of the finest love poetry in our language. The first one is by the famous Scot, Robert Burns.

A RED, RED ROSE

O, my love is like a red, red rose,
　　That's newly sprung in June.
O, my love is like the melody
　　That's sweetly played in tune.

As fair art thou, my bonnie lass,
　　So deep in love am I,
And I will love thee still, my dear,
　　Till all the seas go dry.

Till all the seas go dry, my dear,
　　And the rocks melt with the sun!
And I will love thee still, my dear,
　　While the sands of life shall run.

And fare thee well, my only love,
　　And fare thee well awhile!
And I will come again, my love,
　　Though it were ten thousand mile!

—ROBERT BURNS

Older people, especially parents, caution you about "puppy love," saying that it is an infatuation that will soon pass. Sometimes these elders forget how intense the emotion of love is, whether one is sixteen or sixty. In the next poem Elizabeth Barrett Browning counts the ways in which she feels love's powerful influence.

HOW DO I LOVE THEE?

How do I love thee? Let me count the ways.
I love thee to the depth and breadth and height
My soul can reach, when feeling out of sight
For the ends of Being and Ideal Grace.

I love thee to the level of everyday's
Most quiet need, by sun and candlelight.
I love thee freely, as men strive for Right;
I love thee purely, as they turn from Praise.
I love thee with the passion put to use
In my old griefs, and with my childhood's faith.
I love thee with a love I seemed to lose
With my lost saints—I love thee with the breath,
Smiles, tears, of all my life!—and, if God choose,
I shall but love thee better after death.

—ELIZABETH BARRETT BROWNING

Elizabeth Barrett Browning's love was so deep that it defied time. The final poem of this set of three speaks of a love that has come and gone. Lord Byron describes with poetic sadness a memory of happier times.

SO, WE'LL GO NO MORE A ROVING

So, we'll go no more a roving
    So late into the night,
Though the heart be still as loving,
    And the moon be still as bright.

For the sword outwears its sheath,
    And the soul wears out the breast.
And the heart must pause to breathe,
    And love itself have rest.

Though the night was made for loving,
    And the day returns too soon,
Yet we'll go no more a roving
    By the light of the moon.

—GEORGE GORDON, LORD BYRON

Broken love, disappointment, frustration—all these are as common among young people as among adults. You may have found that there are times when the only way to untangle your thoughts is to get away by yourself. You may take walks, sit by the sea or a lake or in a park, or just find a quiet spot in the house; each person has his own way of being alone when he needs to be, and this need is very real and important.

THE CAVE

Sometimes when the boy was troubled he would go
   To a little cave of stone above the brook
And build a fire just big enough to glow
   Upon the ledge outside, then sit and look.
Below him was the winding silver trail
   Of water from the upland pasture springs,
, And meadows where he heard the calling quail;
   Before him was the sky, and passing wings.

The tang of willow twigs he lighted there,
   Fragrance of meadows breathing slow and deep,
The cave's own musky coolness on the air,
   The scent of sunlight . . . all were his to keep.
We had such places—cave or tree or hill . . .
   And we are lucky if we keep them still.

—GLENN W. DRESBACH

The next poem is not an easy one. The writer speaks of the need to put meaning into one's life. George Gray, about whom the poem is written, did not succeed in making his life truly significant. Now, as he nears death and looks at the inscription to be placed on his tombstone, he makes these statements, which may serve as a guide to you in the years that lie ahead:

GEORGE GRAY

I have studied many times
The marble which was chiseled for me—
A boat with a furled sail at rest in a harbor.
In truth it pictures not my destination
But my life.
For love was offered me and I shrank from its disillusionment;
Sorrow knocked at my door, but I was afraid;
Ambition called to me, but I dreaded the chances.
Yet all the while I hungered for meaning in my life.
And now I know that we must lift the sail
And catch the winds of destiny
Wherever they drive the boat.
To put meaning in one's life may end in madness,
But life without meaning is the torture
Of restlessness and vague desire—
It is a boat longing for the sea and yet afraid.

—EDGAR LEE MASTERS

No one can be sure of what he will remember from his youth, as the years roll by. In the final poem in this chapter, the writer tells of his memories in his old age. Of his many recollections, the most important seem to be the "long, long thoughts" of his youth. Perhaps you, too, as time passes, will remember this quality of your early years with the greatest clarity.

MY LOST YOUTH

Often I think of the beautiful town
    That is seated by the sea;
Often in thought go up and down
The pleasant streets of that dear old town,
    And my youth comes back to me.

And a verse of a Lapland song
Is haunting my memory still:
'A boy's will is the wind's will
And the thoughts of youth are long, long thoughts.'

I can see the shadowy lines of its trees,
And catch, in sudden gleams,
The sheen of the far-surrounding seas,
And islands that were the Hesperides
Of all my boyish dreams.
And the burden of that old song,
It murmurs and whispers still:
'A boy's will is the wind's will,
And the thoughts of youth are long, long thoughts.'

I remember the black wharves and the slips,
And the sea-tides tossing free;
And Spanish sailors with bearded lips,
And the beauty and mystery of the ships,
And the magic of the sea.
And the voice of that wayward song
Is singing and saying still:
'A boy's will is the wind's will,
And the thoughts of youth are long, long thoughts.'

I remember the bulwarks by the shore,
And the fort upon the hill;
The sunrise gun, with its hollow roar,
The drum-beat repeated o'er and o'er,
And the bugle wild and shrill.
And the music of that old song
Throbs in my memory still:
'A boy's will is the wind's will,
And the thoughts of youth are long, long thoughts.'

I remember the sea-fight far away,
    How it thundered o'er the tide!
And the dead captains, as they lay
In their graves, o'erlooking the tranquil bay
    Where they in battle died.
      And the sound of that mournful song
      Goes through me with a thrill:
      'A boy's will is the wind's will,
And the thoughts of youth are long, long thoughts.'

I can see the breezy dome of groves,
    The shadows of Deering's Woods;
And the friendships old and the early loves
Come back with a Sabbath sound, as of doves
    In quiet neighborhoods.
      And the verse of that sweet old song,
      It flutters and murmurs still:
      'A boy's will is the wind's will,
And the thoughts of youth are long, long thoughts.'

I remember the gleams and glooms that dart
    Across the school-boy's brain;
The song and the silence in the heart,
That in part are prophecies, and in part
    Are longings wild and vain.
      And the voice of that fitful song
      Sings on, and is never still:
      'A boy's will is the wind's will,
And the thoughts of youth are long, long thoughts."

There are things of which I may not speak;
    There are dreams that cannot die;
There are thoughts that make the strong heart weak,
And bring a pallor into the cheek,
    And a mist before the eye.

And the words of that fatal song
Come over me like a chill:
'A boy's will is the wind's will,
And the thoughts of youth are long, long thoughts.'

Strange to me now are the forms I meet
When I visit the dear old town;
But the native air is pure and sweet,
And the trees that o'ershadow each well-known street,
As they balance up and down,
Are singing the beautiful song,
Are sighing and whispering still:
'A boy's will is the wind's will,
And the thoughts of youth are long, long thoughts.'

And Deering's Woods are fresh and fair,
And with joy that is almost pain
My heart goes back to wander there,
And among the dreams of the days that were,
I find my lost youth again.
And the strange and beautiful song,
The groves are repeating it still:
'A boy's will is the wind's will,
And the thoughts of youth are long, long thoughts.'

—HENRY WADSWORTH LONGFELLOW

LOOKING BEYOND THE WORDS

1. What does the poet of "Hold Fast Your Dreams!" mean by these words?

Forget the calm that lies
In disillusioned eyes.

2. The ending of "Those Two Boys" may have contained a surprise for you. Explain the author's technique in gaining his humorous effect.

3. "Opportunity" is an optimistic poem. In what ways do you agree or disagree with the poet's outlook?

4. In "The Road Not Taken" what does Robert Frost mean by "knowing how way leads on to way"? How may one's life be shaped by way leading on to way?

5. In "If" Rudyard Kipling lists many qualities of maturity which he believes make certain adults superior to others. Select those characteristics that you feel are the most important and explain why you feel as you do.

6. Explain the final stanza of "Barter." What is your opinion of this view of life? What beliefs do you have that make you agree or disagree with the poet?

7. "Adventure" is a very short poem; yet there is an important thought expressed. What is this thought? What other poem in this chapter has a similar idea?

8. "I Meant to Do My Work Today" is written in a light mood, but it has a more serious side to it. What is the poet saying to you as a young person, especially in the final line?

9. "The Wanderer's Song" speaks about the charm that the sea had for the writer; yet many readers who do not share Masefield's feeling for the sea enjoy this poem. How may the poem be interpreted to give a more general meaning than is at first apparent?

10. The poet of "The Call of the Spring" gives some rather broad advice on living life fully. Summarize this advice in three or four sentences.

11. What is your interpretation of the final stanza of "A Little Song of Life"?

12. Is the writer of "Sixteen" sympathetic to young people, or is she just making fun of them? In what ways do you think she is accurate or inaccurate in her description?

13. Robert Burns's poem "A Red, Red Rose" has contributed much to making the red rose the symbol of love. What did the poet gain by repeating the adjective *red?* How would the poem have lost much of its force without this repetition?

14. Does the kind of love described in Elizabeth Barrett Browning's "How Do I Love Thee?" still exist today? In what ways does modern love differ from Miss Browning's love?

15. In Lord Byron's "So, We'll Go No More A Roving," what are the reasons given for the ending of the love affair? Who ended it—the man or the woman? Why do you think so?

16. In Glenn W. Dresbach's poem what larger meaning does the cave have? Explain the final two lines with this more general interpretation in mind.

17. George Gray has many bitter regrets. If he could live his life again, what particular change would he make in his attitude toward life?

18. Psychologists tell us that we tend to forget the unpleasant thoughts and experiences that we have had, and normally to remember the pleasant. In what way is this tendency demonstrated in "My Lost Youth"? Has the poet completely forgotten all unpleasantness?

CHAPTER FIVE

The Strange and Supernatural

Tales of fantasy and imagination may be found in every country and in every language. Accounts of ghosts and demons, of magic spells and strange happenings, of haunted castles and phantom ships are everywhere. Some of them are as old as the human race. It is not surprising that the poets of our language have written many poems that deal with this dimly-lit world.

You have probably already discovered that the best stories of the supernatural leave a great deal unsaid. Looking for exact answers in the world of mystery takes away much of the charm; so you must be prepared to find that poems that speak of these topics leave much to your imagination, even more than the stories do. Furthermore, it is not always wise to look at these poems with the intention of finding deeper meanings and morals—such a procedure would reduce your enjoyment. Far more than in other types of poetry, poems of the supernatural are meant to create a *mood* or *feeling* that is in itself more important than what is being told. You will find vivid imagery and colorful language to help you journey from reality into this land of legend and mystery, where every wind can bring a lover's ghost or a madman's song.

The poems that follow all deal with unusual topics. A few of them give just a hint of mystery; others seem almost to have been written by the residents of a magic world. You will find some familiar stories, some unfamiliar ones, some strange people, and some strange dreams. If you can arrange it, read the poems at night when you are alone in a quiet house and can appreciate the eerie atmosphere that the poems can create.

The first poem of this section gives just a hint of the magic world to follow. It is not, strictly speaking, a true poem of the supernatural; but it has a touch of mystery about it that will serve well to start you on your way. It is based on a famous legend that dates back to the eighteenth century when bold highwaymen made a mockery of law and order in England. Even today, say the residents of the area, the sounds of the highwayman may be heard on certain nights when the wind is right and the moon shines through the broken clouds.

THE HIGHWAYMAN

PART ONE

The wind was a torrent of darkness among the gusty trees.
The moon was a ghostly galleon tossed upon cloudy seas.
The road was a ribbon of moonlight over the purple moor,
And the highwayman came riding—
        Riding—riding—
The highwayman came riding, up to the old inn-door.

He'd a French cocked-hat on his forehead, a bunch of lace at his chin,
A coat of the claret velvet, and breeches of brown doe-skin.
They fitted with never a wrinkle. His boots were up to the thigh.
And he rode with a jeweled twinkle,
        His pistol butts a-twinkle,
His rapier hilt a-twinkle, under the jeweled sky.

Over the cobbles he clattered and clashed in the dark inn-yard.
He tapped with his whip on the shutters, but all was locked and
    barred.
He whistled a tune to the window, and who should be waiting there
But the landlord's black-eyed daughter,
        Bess, the landlord's daughter,
Plaiting a dark red love-knot into her long black hair.

And dark in the dark old inn-yard a stable-wicket creaked
Where Tim the ostler listened. His face was white and peaked.
His eyes were hollows of madness, his hair like mouldy hay,
But he loved the landlord's daughter,
        The landlord's red-lipped daughter.
Dumb as a dog he listened, and he heard the robber say—

"One kiss, my bonny sweetheart, I'm after a prize tonight,
But I shall be back with the yellow gold before the morning light;
Yet, if they press me sharply, and harry me through the day,

Then look for me by moonlight,
        Watch for me by moonlight,
I'll come to thee by moonlight, though hell should bar the way."

He rose upright in the stirrups. He scarce could reach her hand,
But she loosened her hair in the casement. His face burnt like a brand
As the black cascade of perfume came tumbling over his breast;
And he kissed its waves in the moonlight,
        (O, sweet black waves in the moonlight!)
Then he tugged at his rein in the moonlight, and galloped away to the
    west.

PART TWO

He did not come in the dawning. He did not come at noon;
And out of the tawny sunset, before the rise of the moon,
When the road was a gypsy's ribbon, looping the purple moor,
A red-coat troop came marching—
        Marching—marching—
King George's men came marching, up to the old inn-door.

They said no word to the landlord. They drank his ale instead.
But they gagged his daughter, and bound her, to the foot of her
    narrow bed.
Two of them knelt at her casement, with muskets at their side!
There was death at every window;
        And hell at one dark window;
For Bess could see, through her casement, the road that *he* would
    ride.

They had tied her up to attention, with many a sniggering jest.
They had bound a musket beside her, with the muzzle beneath her
    breast!

"Now, keep good watch!" and they kissed her. She heard the doomed
  man say—
Look for me by moonlight;
      Watch for me by moonlight;
I'll come to thee by moonlight, though hell should bar the way!

She twisted her hands behind her; but all the knots held good!
She writhed her hands till her fingers were wet with sweat or blood!
They stretched and strained in the darkness, and the hours crawled
  by like years,
Till, now, on the stroke of midnight,
      Cold, on the stroke of midnight,
The tip of one finger touched it! The trigger at least was hers!

The tip of one finger touched it. She strove no more for the rest.
Up, she stood to attention, with the muzzle beneath her breast.
She would not risk their hearing; she would not strive again;
For the road lay bare in the moonlight;
      Blank and bare in the moonlight;
And the blood of her veins, in the moonlight, throbbed to her love's
  refrain.

Tlot-tlot, tlot-tlot! Had they heard it? The horse hoofs ringing clear;
Tlot-tlot, tlot-tlot, in the distance? Were they deaf that they did not
  hear?
Down the ribbon of moonlight, over the brow of the hill,
The highwayman came riding—
      Riding—riding—
The red-coats looked to their priming! She stood up, straight and still.

Tlot-tlot, in the frosty silence! *Tlot-tlot,* in the echoing night!
Nearer he came and nearer. Her face was like a light.
Her eyes grew wide for a moment; she drew one last deep breath,

Then her finger moved in the moonlight,
        Her musket shattered the moonlight,
Shattered her breast in the moonlight and warned him—with her
   death.

He turned. He spurred to the west; he did not know who stood
Bowed, with her head o'er the musket, drenched with her own blood!
Not till the dawn he heard it, and his face grew grey to hear
How Bess, the landlord's daughter,
        The landlord's black-eyed daughter,
Had watched for her love in the moonlight, and died in the darkness
   there.

Back, he spurred like a madman, shouting a curse to the sky,
With the white road smoking behind him and his rapier brandished
   high.
Blood-red were his spurs in the golden noon; wine-red was his velvet
   coat;
When they shot him down on the highway,
        Down like a dog on the highway,
And he lay in his blood on the highway, with a bunch of lace at his
   throat.

And still of a winter's night, they say, when the wind is in the trees,
When the moon is a ghostly galleon tossed upon cloudy seas,
When the road is a ribbon of moonlight over the purple moor,
A highwayman comes riding—
        Riding—riding—
A highwayman comes riding, up to the old inn-door.

Over the cobbles he clatters and clangs in the dark inn-yard.
He taps with his whip on the shutters, but all is locked and barred.

He whistles a tune to the window, and who should be waiting there
But the landlord's black-eyed daughter,
　　　　Bess, the landlord's daughter,
Plaiting a dark red love-knot into her long black hair.

—ALFRED NOYES

Almost every young person knows the stories of Robin Hood and his merry band. Robin has been dead now for hundreds of years, but his ghost and the ghosts of his followers still haunt their woodland home in Sherwood Forest.

A SONG OF SHERWOOD

Sherwood in the twilight, is Robin Hood awake?
Gray and ghostly shadows are gliding through the brake;
Shadows of the dappled deer, dreaming of the morn,
Dreaming of a shadowy man that winds a shadowy horn.

Robin Hood is here again: all his merry thieves
Hear a ghostly bugle-note shivering through the leaves,
Calling as he used to call, faint and far away,
In Sherwood, in Sherwood, about the break of day.

Merry, merry England has kissed the lips of June:
All the wings of fairyland were here beneath the moon;
Like a flight of rose-leaves fluttering in a mist
Of opal and ruby and pearl and amethyst.

Merry, merry England is waking as of old,
With eyes of blither hazel and hair of brighter gold:
For Robin Hood is here again beneath the bursting spray
In Sherwood, in Sherwood, about the break of day.

Love is in the greenwood building him a house
Of wild rose and hawthorn and honeysuckle boughs;
Love is in the greenwood: dawn is in the skies;
And Marian is waiting with a glory in her eyes.

Hark! The dazzled laverock climbs the golden steep:
Marian is waiting: is Robin Hood asleep?
Round the fairy grass-rings frolic elf and fay,
In Sherwood, in Sherwood, about the break of day.

Oberon, Oberon, rake away the gold,
Rake away the red leaves, roll away the mold,
Rake away the gold leaves, roll away the red,
And wake Will Scarlet from his leafy forest bed.

Friar Tuck and Little John are riding down together
With quarter-staff and drinking-can and gray goose-feather;
The dead are coming back again; the years are rolled away
In Sherwood, in Sherwood, about the break of day.

Softly over Sherwood the south wind blows;
All the heart of England hid in every rose
Hears across the greenwood the sunny whisper leap,
Sherwood in the red dawn, is Robin Hood asleep?

Hark the voice of England wakes him as of old
And, shattering the silence with a cry of brighter gold,
Bugles in the greenwood echo from the steep,
Sherwood in the red dawn, is Robin Hood asleep?

Where the deer are gliding down the shadowy glen
All across the glades of fern he calls his merry men;
Doublets of the Lincoln green glancing through the May,
In Sherwood, in Sherwood, about the break of day;

Calls them and they answer: from aisles of oak and ash
Rings the *Follow! Follow!* and the boughs begin to crash;
The ferns begin to flutter and the flowers begin to fly;
And through the crimson dawning the robber band goes by.

Robin! Robin! Robin! All his merry thieves
Answer as the bugle-note shivers through the leaves:
Calling as he used to call, faint and far away,
In Sherwood, in Sherwood, about the break of day.

—ALFRED NOYES

A most remarkable American, Daniel Webster, was such an unusual and powerful personality in his time that he has become a
legendary figure in our history. The next poem tells one of the many
stories about him, and you will see the spirit of defiance that set
Webster apart from other men.

DANIEL WEBSTER'S HORSES

If when the wind blows
    Rattling the trees,
Clicking like skeletons'
    Elbows and knees,

You hear along the road
    Three horses pass,
Do not go near the dark
    Cold window-glass.

If when the first snow lies
    Whiter than bones,
You see the mark of hoofs
    Cut to the stones,

Hoofs of three horses
    Going abreast—
Turn about, turn about,
    A closed door is best!

Upright in the earth
    Under the sod
They buried three horses,
    Bridled and shod,

Daniel Webster's horses—
    He said as he grew old,
"Flesh, I loved riding,
    Shall I not love it cold?

"Shall I not love to ride
    Bone astride bone,
When the cold wind blows
    And snow covers stone?

"Bury them on their feet
    With bridle and bit.
They were good horses—
    See their shoes fit."

                    —ELIZABETH J. COATSWORTH

    The strange and mysterious have a fascination that is sometimes
lost when the facts come to light. In the following poem, however, no
light shines, and you are left to wonder. Can you explain the mystery?

A LADY COMES TO AN INN

Three strange men came to the Inn,
one was a black man, pocked and thin,
one was brown with a silver knife,
and one brought with him a beautiful wife.

That lovely woman had hair as pale
as French champagne or finest ale,
that lovely woman was long and slim
as a young white birch or a maple limb.

Her face was like cream, her mouth was a rose,
what language she spoke nobody knows,
but sometimes she'd scream like a cockatoo
and swear wonderful oaths that nobody knew.

Her great silk skirts like a silver bell
down to her little bronze slippers fell,
and her low-cut gown showed a dove on its nest
in blue tattooing across her breast.

Nobody learned the lady's name
nor the marvelous land from which they came,
but still they tell through all the countryside
the tale of those men and that beautiful bride.

ELIZABETH J. COATSWORTH

The next poem, written by Elinor Wylie, would be difficult to understand without its title. The poet apparently wishes to escape from the struggles of everyday life and enter a fairy world where no one can find or trouble her. Perhaps you, too, have had the same longing when the demands on you seemed too heavy to bear.

ESCAPE

When foxes eat the last gold grape,
And the last white antelope is killed,
I shall stop fighting and escape
Into a little house I'll build.

But first I'll shrink to fairy size,
With a whisper no one understands,
Making blind moons of all your eyes,
And muddy roads of all your hands.

And you may grope for me in vain
In hollows under the mangrove root,
Or where, in apple-scented rain,
The silver wasp-nests hang like fruit.

—ELINOR WYLIE

Here is another poem in which the truth will be forever clouded. When all the night-sounds have been traced, one sound still remains beyond explaining.

SOMEONE

Someone came knocking
        At my wee, small door;
Someone came knocking,
        I'm sure—sure—sure;
I listened, I opened,
        I looked to left and right,
But nought there was a-stirring
        In the still dark night;

Only the busy beetle
    Tap-tapping in the wall,
Only from the forest
    The screech-owl's call,
Only the cricket whistling
    While the dewdrops fall,
So I know not who came knocking,
    At all, at all, at all.

—WALTER DE LA MARE

If you have ever wandered around an old, deserted house, you will recognize the feeling of hopelessness and loneliness that this poem evokes.

THE HOUSE ON THE HILL

They are all gone away,
    The House is shut and still,
There is nothing more to say.

Through broken walls and gray
    The winds blow bleak and shrill:
They are all gone away.

Nor is there one to-day
    To speak them good or ill:
There is nothing more to say.

Why is it then we stray
    Around that sunken sill?
They are all gone away,

And our poor fancy-play
    For them is wasted skill:
There is nothing more to say.

There is ruin and decay
    In the House on the Hill:
They are all gone away,
There is nothing more to say.

—EDWIN ARLINGTON ROBINSON

Have you ever been suddenly touched by an unexplained and disturbing mood? Most of the time you can understand your feelings, if you really try; but every now and then a strange mood settles upon you for a while and then moves on, leaving you to wonder why it came and why it went.

THE SLEEPER

As Ann came in one summer's day,
    She felt that she must creep,
So silent was the clear cool house,
    It seemed a house of sleep.
And sure, when she pushed open the door,
    Rapt in the stillness there,
Her mother sat with stooping head,
    Asleep upon a chair;
Fast—fast asleep; her two hands laid
    Loose-folded on her knee,
So that her small unconscious face
    Looked half unreal to be:
So calmly lit with sleep's pale light
    Each feature was; so fair
Her forehead—every trouble was
Smooth'd out beneath her hair.
But though her mind in dream now moved,
    Still seemed her gaze to rest
From out beneath her fast-sealed lids,
    Above her moving breast,

On Ann, as quite, quite still she stood;
    Yet slumber lay so deep
Even her hands upon her lap
    Seemed saturate with sleep.
And as Ann peeped, a cloudlike dread
    Stole over her, and then,
On stealthy, mouselike feet she trod,
    And tiptoed out again.

              —WALTER DE LA MARE

Another poem by Walter de la Mare seems to tell a fairly straight-
forward story, although of an unusual nature. Old-timers such as
Sam do like to spin yarns, often about strange episodes in their lives.
This poem speaks of a mermaid, but it may be that there is more to
the story than at first appears.

SAM

When Sam goes back in memory,
    It is to where the sea
Breaks on the shingle, emerald-green,
    In white foam, endlessly;
He says—with small brown eye on mine—
    "I used to keep awake,
And lean from my window in the moon,
    Watching those billows break.
And half a million tiny hands,
    And eyes, like sparks of frost,
Would dance and come tumbling into the moon,
    On every breaker tossed.
And all across from star to star,
    I've seen the watery sea,
With not a single ship in sight;
    Just ocean there, and me;

And heard my father snore. And once,
    As sure as I'm alive,
Out of those wallowing, moon-flecked waves
    I saw a mermaid dive;
Head and shoulders above the wave,
    Plain as I now see you,
Combing her hair, now back, now front,
    Her two eyes peeping through;
Calling me, 'Sam!'—quietlike—'Sam!' . . .
    But me . . . I never went,
Making believe I kind of thought
    'Twas someone else she meant . . .
Wonderful lovely there she sat,
    Singing the night away,
All in the solitudinous sea
    Of that there lonely bay.
P'raps," and he'd smooth his hairless mouth,
    "P'raps, if 'twere now, my son,
P'raps, if I heard a voice say, 'Sam!'
    Morning would find me gone."

—WALTER DE LA MARE

Sam, in the poem you have just read, looks back on an event that could have changed his whole life. In "Madman's Song" Elinor Wylie is suggesting in another way that you listen to the call of the strange and unusual.

MADMAN'S SONG

Better to see your cheek grown hollow,
Better to see your temple worn,
Than to forget to follow, follow,
After the sound of a silver horn.

Better to bind your brow with willow
And follow, follow until you die,
Than to sleep with your head on a golden pillow,
Nor lift it up when the hunt goes by.

Better to see your cheek grown sallow
And your hair grown gray, so soon, so soon,
Than to forget to hallo, hallo,
After the milk-white hounds of the moon.

—ELINOR WYLIE

The next poem pictures death as an important figure. Notice, as you read it, how often the hard coldness of stone finds its way into the language and description.

THE STONE

"And will you cut a stone for him,
To set above his head?
And will you cut a stone for him—
A stone for him?" she said.

Three days before, a splintered rock
Had struck her lover dead—
Had struck him in the quarry dead,
Where, careless of the warning call,
He loitered, while the shot was fired—
A lively stripling, brave and tall,
And sure of all his heart desired . . .
A flash, a shock,
A rumbling fall . . .
And, broken 'neath the broken rock,
A lifeless heap, with face of clay,

And still as any stone he lay,
With eyes that saw the end of all.

I went to break the news to her:
And I could hear my own heart beat
With dread of what my lips might say;
But some poor fool had sped before;
And, flinging wide her father's door,
Had blurted out the news to her,
Had struck her lover dead for her,
Had struck the girl's heart dead in her,
Had struck life, lifeless, at a word,
And dropped it at her feet:
Then hurried on his witless way,
Scarce knowing she had heard.

And when I came, she stood alone—
A woman, turned to stone:
And, though no word at all she said,
I knew that all was known.
Because her heart was dead,
She did not sigh nor moan.
His mother wept:
She could not weep.
Her lover slept:
She could not sleep.
Three days, three nights,
She did not stir:
Three days, three nights,
Were one to her,
Who never closed her eyes
From sunset to sunrise,
From dawn to evenfall—
Her tearless, staring eyes,
That, seeing naught, saw all.

The fourth night when I came from work,
I found her at my door.
"And will you cut a stone for him?"
She said: and spoke no more:
But followed me, as I went in,
And sank upon a chair;
And fixed her gray eyes on my face,
With still, unseeing stare.
And, as she waited patiently,
I could not bear to feel
Those still, gray eyes that followed me,
Those eyes that plucked the heart from me,
Those eyes that sucked the breath from me
And curdled the warm blood in me,
Those eyes that cut me to the bone,
And pierced my marrow like cold steel.

And so I rose, and sought a stone;
And cut it, smooth and square:
And, as I worked, she sat and watched,
Beside me, in her chair.
Night after night, by candlelight,
I cut her lover's name:
Night after night, so still and white,
And like a ghost she came;
And sat beside me, in her chair,
And watched with eyes aflame.

She eyed each stroke,
And hardly stirred:
She never spoke
A single word:
And not a sound or murmur broke
The quiet, save the mallet-stroke.

With still eyes ever on my hands,
With eyes that seemed to burn my hands,
My wincing, overwearied hands,
She watched, with bloodless lips apart,
And silent, indrawn breath:
And every stroke my chisel cut,
Death cut still deeper in her heart:
The two of us were chiseling,
Together, I and death.

And when at length the job was done,
And I had laid the mallet by,
As if, at last, her peace were won,
She breathed his name; and, with a sigh,
Passed slowly through the open door:
And never crossed my threshold more.

Next night I labored late, alone,
To cut her name upon the stone.

—W. W. GIBSON

All through recorded history there have been stories about witches. In fact, until quite recently, belief in the existence of witches, or "hags," was commonplace. Three hundred years ago, Robert Herrick wrote the next poem, describing the hag as she was imagined to be by many of the people of that day.

THE HAG

The hag is astride
This night for to ride,
The devil and she together;
Through thick and through thin,
Now out, and then in,
Though ne'er so foul be the weather.

A thorn or a burr
She takes for a spur,
With a lash of a bramble she rides now;
Through brakes and through briars,
O'er ditches and mires,
She follows the spirit that guides now.

No beast for his food
Dares now range the wood,
But hushed in his lair he lies lurking:
While mischiefs by these,
On land and on seas,
At noon of night are a-working.

The storm will arise
And trouble the skies
This night; and, more the wonder,
The ghost from the tomb
Affrighted shall come,
Called out by the clap of the thunder.

—ROBERT HERRICK

Sometimes in poetry the supernatural takes on a spiritual tone. In "The Ballad of the Harp-Weaver" the story reaches its climax with a strange and beautiful event on Christmas Eve.

THE BALLAD OF THE HARP-WEAVER

"Son," said my mother,
When I was knee-high,
"You've need of clothes to cover you,
And not a rag have I.

"There's nothing in the house
To make a boy breeches,
Nor shears to cut a cloth with,
Nor thread to take stitches.

"There's nothing in the house
    But a loaf-end of rye,
And a harp with a woman's head
    Nobody will buy,"
    And she began to cry.

That was in the early fall.
    When came the late fall,
"Son," she said, "the sight of you
    Makes your mother's blood crawl,

"Little skinny shoulder-blades
    Sticking through your clothes!
And where you'll get a jacket from
    God above knows.

"It's lucky for me, lad,
    Your daddy's in the ground,
And can't see the way I let
    His son go around!"
    And she made a queer sound.

That was in the late fall.
    When the winter came,
I'd not a pair of breeches
    Nor a shirt to my name.

I couldn't go to school,
    Or out of doors to play.
And all the other little boys
    Passed our way.

"Son," said my mother,
    "Come, climb into my lap,
And I'll chafe your little bones
    While you take a nap."

And, oh, but we were silly
    For half an hour or more,
Me with my long legs
    Dragging on the floor,

A rock-rock-rocking
    To a mother-goose rhyme!
Oh, but we were happy
    For half an hour's time!

But there was I, a great boy,
    And what would folks say
To hear my mother singing me
    To sleep all day,
    In such a daft way?

Men say the winter
    Was bad that year;
Fuel was scarce,
    And food was dear.

A wind with a wolf's head
    Howled about our door,
And we burned up the chairs
    And sat upon the floor.

All that was left us
    Was a chair we couldn't break,
And the harp with a woman's head
    Nobody would take,
    For song or pity's sake.

The night before Christmas
    I cried with the cold,
I cried myself to sleep
    Like a two-year-old.

And in the deep night
    I felt my mother rise,
And stare down upon me
    With love in her eyes.

I saw my mother sitting
    On the one good chair,
A light falling on her
    From I couldn't tell where,

Looking nineteen,
    And not a day older,
And the harp with a woman's head
    Leaned against her shoulder.

Her thin fingers, moving
    In the thin, tall strings,
Were weav-weav-weaving
    Wonderful things.

Many bright threads,
    From where I couldn't see,
Were running through the harp-strings
    Rapidly,

And gold threads whistling
    Through my mother's hand.
I saw the web grow,
    And the pattern expand.

She wove a child's jacket,
    And when it was done
She laid it on the floor
    And wove another one.

She wove a red cloak
　　So regal to see,
"She's made it for a king's son,"
　　I said, "and not for me."
　　But I knew it was for me.

She wove a pair of breeches
　　Quicker than that!
She wove a pair of boots
　　And a little cocked hat.

She wove a pair of mittens,
　　She wove a little blouse,
She wove all night
　　In the still, cold house.

She sang as she worked,
　　And the harp-strings spoke;
Her voice never faltered,
　　And the thread never broke.
　　And when I awoke,—

There sat my mother
　　With the harp against her shoulder,
Looking nineteen,
　　And not a day older,

A smile about her lips,
　　And a light about her head,
And her hands in the harp-strings
　　Frozen dead.

And piled up beside her
　　And toppling to the skies,
Were the clothes of a king's son,
　　Just my size.

　　　　　　　　—EDNA ST. VINCENT MILLAY

It is not often that you will be able to hear an argument between two inhabitants of another world, the "half-world" where dwell the "little people." Harold Monro reports such an argument in this next poem, one of the most delicate of all poems of the supernatural.

OVERHEARD ON A SALTMARSH

Nymph, nymph, what are your beads?

Green glass, goblin. Why do you stare at them?

Give them me.

       No.

Give them me. Give them me.

       No.

Then I will howl all night in the reeds,
Lie in the mud and howl for them.

Goblin, why do you love them so?

They are better than stars or water,
Better than voices of winds that sing,
Better than any man's fair daughter,
Your green glass beads on a silver ring.

Hush, I stole them out of the moon.
Give me your beads, I desire them.

       No.

I will howl in a deep lagoon
For your green glass beads, I love them so.
Give them me. Give them.

       No.

—HAROLD MONRO

The last of these poems is Edgar Allen Poe's "The Raven." Poe, thought by many to be America's best writer of stories and poems of the strange and supernatural, gives his imagination free rein in this famous poem.

THE RAVEN

Once upon a midnight dreary, while I pondered, weak and weary,
Over many a quaint and curious volume of forgotten lore—
While I nodded, nearly napping, suddenly there came a tapping,
As of someone gently rapping, rapping at my chamber door.
" 'Tis some visitor," I muttered, "tapping at my chamber door—
Only this and nothing more."

Ah, distinctly I remember it was in the bleak December,
And each separate dying ember wrought its ghost upon the floor.
Eagerly I wished the morrow;—vainly I had sought to borrow
From my books surcease of sorrow—sorrow for the lost Lenore—
For the rare and radiant maiden whom the angels name Lenore—
Nameless *here* for evermore.

And the silken, sad, uncertain rustling of each purple curtain
Thrilled me—filled me with fantastic terrors never felt before;
So that now, to still the beating of my heart, I stood repeating,
" 'Tis some visitor entreating entrance at my chamber door,
Some late visitor entreating entrance at my chamber door;—
This it is and nothing more."

Presently my soul grew stronger; hesitating then no longer,
"Sir," said I, "or Madam, truly your forgiveness I implore;
But the fact is I was napping, and so gently you came rapping,
And so faintly you came tapping, tapping at my chamber door,
That I scarce was sure I heard you"—here I opened wide the door—
Darkness there and nothing more.

Deep into that darkness peering, long I stood there wondering, fearing,
Doubting, dreaming dreams no mortal ever dared to dream before;
But the silence was unbroken, and the stillness gave no token,
And the only word there spoken was the whispered word, "Lenore!"
This I whispered, and an echo murmured back the word, "Lenore!"
Merely this and nothing more.

Back into the chamber turning, all my soul within me burning,
Soon again I heard a tapping somewhat louder than before.
"Surely," said I, "surely that is something at my window lattice;
Let me see, then, what thereat is, and this mystery explore—
Let my heart be still a moment and this mystery explore—
'Tis the wind and nothing more."

Open here I flung the shutter, when, with many a flirt and flutter,
In there stepped a stately Raven of the saintly days of yore.
Not the least obeisance made he; not a minute stopped or stayed he;
But with mien of lord or lady perched above my chamber door—
Perched upon a bust of Pallas just above my chamber door—
Perched, and sat, and nothing more.

Then this ebony bird beguiling my sad fancy into smiling
By the grave and stern decorum of the countenance it wore,
"Though thy crest be shorn and shaven, thou," I said, "art sure no craven,
Ghastly grim and ancient Raven wandering from the Nightly shore—
Tell me what thy lordly name is on the Night's Plutonian shore!"
Quoth the Raven, "Nevermore."

Much I marvelled this ungainly fowl to hear discourse so plainly,
Though its answer little meaning—little relevancy bore;
For we cannot help agreeing that no living human being
Ever yet was blessed with seeing bird above his chamber door—
Bird or beast upon the sculptured bust above his chamber door,
With such name as "Nevermore."

But the Raven, sitting lonely on the placid bust, spoke only
That one word, as if his soul in that one word he did outpour.
Nothing further then he uttered—not a feather then he fluttered—
Till I scarcely more than muttered, "Other friends have flown before;
On the morrow *he* will leave me, as my hopes have flown before."
            Then the bird said, "Nevermore."

Startled at the stillness broken by reply so aptly spoken,
"Doubtless," said I, "what it utters is its only stock and store,
Caught from some unhappy master whom unmerciful Disaster
Followed fast and followed faster till his songs one burden bore—
Till the dirges of his Hope that melancholy burden bore
            Of 'Never—nevermore.' "

But the Raven still beguiling all my fancy into smiling,
Straight I wheeled a cushioned seat in front of bird, and bust and door;
Then, upon the velvet sinking, I betook myself to linking
Fancy unto fancy, thinking what this ominous bird of yore—
What this grim, ungainly, ghastly, gaunt, and ominous bird of yore
            Meant in croaking "Nevermore."

This I sat engaged in guessing, but no syllable expressing
To the fowl, whose fiery eyes now burned into my bosom's core;
This and more I sat divining, with my head at ease reclining
On the cushion's velvet lining that the lamplight gloated o'er,
But whose velvet violet lining with the lamplight gloating o'er
            She shall press, ah, nevermore!

Then, methought, the air grew denser, perfumed from an unseen
            censer
Swung by Seraphim whose foot-falls tinkled on the tufted floor.

"Wretch," I cried, "thy God hath lent thee—by these angels he hath
  sent thee
Respite—respite and nepenthe from thy memories of Lenore!
Quaff, oh, quaff this kind nepenthe, and forget this lost Lenore!"
            Quoth the Raven, "Nevermore."

"Prophet!" said I, "thing of evil! prophet still, if bird or devil!—
Whether Tempter sent, or whether tempest tossed thee here ashore,
Desolate yet all undaunted, on this desert land enchanted—
On this home by Horror haunted—tell me truly, I implore—
Is there—*is* there balm in Gilead?—tell me—tell me, I implore!"
            Quoth the Raven, "Nevermore."

"Prophet!" said I, "thing of evil!—prophet still, if bird or devil!
By that Heaven that bends above us—by that God we both adore,
Tell this soul with sorrow laden if, within the distant Aidenn,
It shall clasp a sainted maiden whom the angels name Lenore—
Clasp a rare and radiant maiden whom the angels name Lenore!"
            Quoth the Raven, "Nevermore."

"Be that word our sign of parting, bird or fiend!" I shrieked, up-
  starting—
"Get thee back into the tempest and the Night's Plutonian shore!
Leave no black plume as a token of that lie thy soul hath spoken!
Leave my loneliness unbroken!—quit the bust above my door!
Take thy beak from out my heart, and take thy form from off my
  door!"
            Quoth the Raven, "Nevermore."

And the Raven, never flitting, still is sitting, *still* is sitting
On the pallid bust of Pallas just above my chamber door;
And his eyes have all the seeming of a demon's that is dreaming,

And the lamplight o'er him streaming throws his shadow on the
  floor;
And my soul from out that shadow that lies floating on the floor
                  Shall be lifted—nevermore!

                                        —EDGAR ALLAN POE.

LOOKING BEYOND THE WORDS

1. What was it that caused "King George's men" to be waiting for the highwayman when he rode back to see Bess in the moonlight?

2. Alfred Noyes, the author of this poem, repeated the first two stanzas of the poem at the very end. What purpose was served by this repetition?

3. Pick out some of the words and phrases in "A Song of Sherwood" which contribute to the ghostly effect of this poem.

4. How does the choice of the "break of day" as the time-setting for the poem help to produce the effect achieved by Alfred Noyes?

5. Why was Daniel Webster so particular that his horses be well-shod and buried upright?

6. Why do you think the poet chose to use short, sharp lines and a brisk rhythm in "Daniel Webster's Horses"?

7. "A Lady Comes to an Inn" is filled with similes and metaphors. List several such figures of speech that catch your eye.

8. Do you feel that the poem gains or loses by not being more specific? What would happen if you learned where the three men and the lady came from and where they went? Explain.

9. What particular things are mentioned in "Escape" which create a feeling of make-believe and unreality?

10. What do you suppose are some of the reasons why the author of this poem wants to escape? If it were you, why would you like to get away?

11. Many images in "Someone" seem to give the effect of smallness. Point out some which give you a feeling that everything is little in this picture.

12. Have you ever heard sounds in the night that caused strange feelings in you? Write one or two paragraphs (or a short poem) describing an experience of this sort.

13. "The House on the Hill" is unusual in the way it rhymes. Look at the poem carefully and describe the rhyme-pattern, pointing out what lines rhyme with what other lines.

14. How do you think the repeated lines contribute to the feeling of loneliness that the poet wants to convey?

15. Notice how many words in "The Sleeper" suggest quietness, calmness, sleep. See how many you can find that add to the effect of stillness.

16. What do you think was the nature of the "cloudlike dread" that disturbed Ann and caused her to leave the house so quietly?

17. What does Walter de la Mare refer to when he speaks of "the moon" in line seven and again in line eleven of "Sam"?

18. As the years passed after he had ignored the mermaid's call, Sam came to give the mermaid a special importance. What do you think she means to him, and why does he say he would probably answer if she called to him again?

19. What do the "silver horn," "the hunt," and the "milk-white hounds of the moon" stand for in "Madman's Song"?

20. Write a short paragraph showing how the last few lines of "Sam" and the last stanza of "Madman's Song" suggest much the same idea.

21. The last two lines of "The Stone" suggest a great deal. What does the poet tell us in these two lines? Why does he say "*the* stone" instead of "*a* stone"?

22. How many ways can you find in which the title of this poem has meaning in the story? There are several ways in which the poet uses "stone" to stand for more than stone itself.

23. In "The Hag" what is the "spirit that guides"? How do you explain the words "the devil and she together"?

24. Compare our image of "witches" today with that of Robert Herrick's time, more than three centuries ago.

25. Describe the situation in "The Ballad of the Harp-Weaver" in which the mother and her son found themselves, and which forced the mother to make her sacrifice.

26. What were the signs that made the boy aware that supernatural forces were at work during the remarkable night before Christmas?

27. In "Overheard on a Saltmarsh," to whom do the two voices belong? Which lines are spoken by each of the voices?

28. Write a paragraph describing how you see the setting—the time and the place—of this overheard conversation.

29. Who do you think Lenore might have been? What is it for which the poet longs that will happen "nevermore"?

30. The raven itself may have several symbolic meanings. What do you think it stands for? Explain.

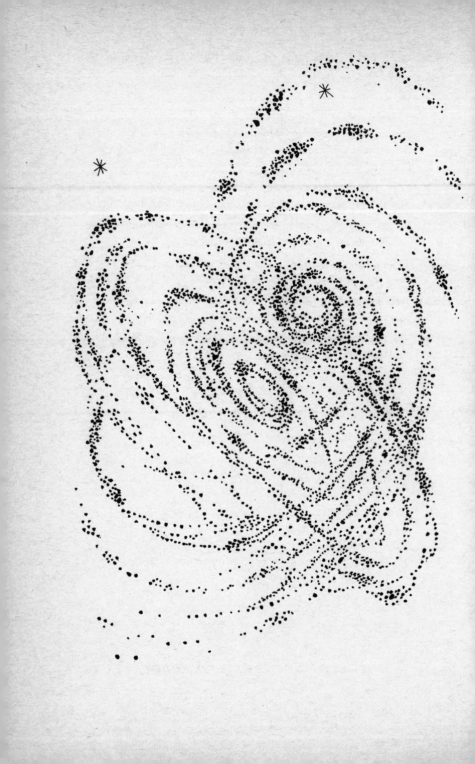

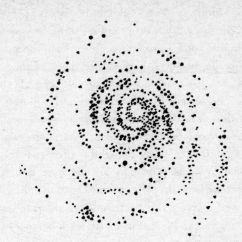

CHAPTER SIX
Personal Belief

Early in this book it was stated that poets are, and have always been, a group of thoughtful, keenly sensitive people. You will remember how necessary it is, if they are to be fine poets, that they become especially good observers of life. Their deep, profound thoughts of this life, however, have caused many of them to examine certain basic, age-old questions: Why are we born? Is there a higher power which shapes our lives? If there is such a power, how much or how little does it rule us? What is *truly* a "good" or "bad" action? What is the purpose behind our being alive in this world? Such questions are important to many thoughtful people; they are particularly important to poets. You may already have noticed that some of the poets have been deeply concerned with the ultimate mystery of death, that undiscovered country from which no traveller returns. Because of their interest in life and its mysteries, a number of poets have written about spiritual matters.

In the course of their thinking about the larger meanings and purposes of life, *they have composed poetry that, whether or not it reflects exactly the personal beliefs you hold to be true, is of outstanding literary merit.* The poets clearly do not agree with one another in these spiritual matters, and many highly individualized views have been included in this chapter.

Such differences of opinion among the poets are entirely understandable when you recall that the poet writes primarily for himself. He may have the viewpoint of a religious faith that is the same as that of his friends and his community, or his beliefs may be quite different from those of most of the people he knows. Certainly, even if he so wished, he could not write of a particular faith with all people in mind; there are too many differences of opinion concerning spiritual beliefs. Whatever the poet's reasons, or whatever his faith (or seeming lack of faith), from spiritual inspiration has come some of the finest poetry of our language. The writing of poetry is in many ways a very honest activity: the written product of the poet's mind must stand or fall on its literary merit; and when a writer speaks privately of his Maker or his own faith, it is an intensely personal statement that deserves your respect, whatever your personal beliefs may be.

Common to most poets, as you surely have noticed, is love of nature. Some poets have been so impressed with the beauty of nature that they have found in it glorious evidence of a divine force behind creation. Emily Dickinson, who lived in New England during a period when formal church service was lengthy, preferred to spend her Sundays close to nature, as this poem shows:

SOME KEEP THE SABBATH

Some keep the Sabbath going to church;
I keep it staying at home,
With a bobolink for a chorister,
And an orchard for a dome.

Some keep the Sabbath in surplice;
I just wear my wings;
And instead of tolling the bell for church,
Our little sexton sings.

God preaches,—a noted clergyman,—
And the sermon is never long;
So instead of getting to heaven at last,
I'm going all along!

—EMILY DICKINSON

A good many years before Miss Dickinson, the English poet William Wordsworth regarded nature in a somewhat similar fashion. He responded to its beauty in this way:

MY HEART LEAPS UP

My heart leaps up when I behold
  A rainbow in the sky;
So was it when my life began;
So is it now I am a man;
So be it when I shall grow old.
  Or let me die!
The Child is father of the Man;
And I could wish my days to be
Bound each to each by natural piety.

—WILLIAM WORDSWORTH

A more modern poet, Edna St. Vincent Millay, was aware of the great influence that nature could exert upon man. You may on occasion have felt a similar response, perhaps when you visited the seashore, a park, or a woodland area. In the next poem, Miss Millay reveals the almost breathless adoration that nature sometimes aroused in her:

GOD'S WORLD

O world, I cannot hold thee close enough!
  Thy winds, thy wide gray skies!
  Thy mists, that roll and rise!
Thy woods, this autumn day, that ache and sag
And all but cry with colour! That gaunt crag
To crush! To lift the lean of that black bluff!
World, World, I cannot get thee close enough!
Long have I known a glory in it all,
  But never knew I this:
  Here such a passion is

As stretcheth me apart,—Lord, I do fear
Thou'st made the world too beautiful this year;
My soul is all but out of me,—let fall
No burning leaf; prithee, let no bird call.

—EDNA ST. VINCENT MILLAY

In "God's World," Miss Millay wrote of the beauty of nature. In the next poem, Walter de la Mare looks at nature from a different standpoint, comparing his inability to see the great power behind the universe to the inability of lesser creatures to see him. It is an interesting and illuminating poem, a fine example of the way a poet can express a profound idea in simple language.

ALL BUT BLIND

> All but blind
> > In his chambered hole
> Gropes for worms
> > The four-clawed Mole.
>
> All but blind
> > In the evening sky,
> The hooded Bat
> > Twirls softly by.
>
> All but blind
> > In the burning day
> The Barn-Owl blunders
> > On her way.
>
> And blind as are
> > These three to me,
> So, blind to Someone
> > I must be.

—WALTER DE LA MARE

In religious history the humble donkey had one "fierce hour and sweet." If you read the next poem carefully, you will recognize when this moment occurred, and why the donkey is not dismayed at his appearance or his humble role in life.

THE DONKEY

When fishes flew and forests walked
    And figs grew upon thorn,
Some moment when the moon was blood
    Then surely I was born.

With monstrous head and sickening cry
    And ears like errant wings,
The devil's walking parody
    Of all four-footed things.

The tattered outlaw of the earth,
    Of ancient crooked will;
Starve, scourge, deride me: I am dumb,
    I keep my secret still.

Fools! For I also had my hour;
    One far fierce hour and sweet:
There was a shout about my ears,
    And palms before my feet.

—G. K. CHESTERTON

"The Tiger" is one of the most familiar poems in English literature. Nearly all well-read people can quote the first stanza, with its almost hypnotic language. In it the poet expresses wonder at the remarkable contrast between the awesome power and the gentle delicacy of the creative force in the universe.

THE TIGER

Tiger! Tiger! burning bright
In the forests of the night,
What immortal hand or eye
Could frame thy fearful symmetry?

In what distant deeps or skies
Burnt the fire of thine eyes?
On what wings dare he aspire?
What the hand dare seize the fire?

And what shoulder, and what art,
Could twist the sinews of thy heart?
And when thy heart began to beat,
What dread hand? and what dread feet?

What the hammer? what the chain?
In what furnace was thy brain?
What the anvil? what dread grasp
Dare its deadly terrors clasp?

When the stars threw down their spears,
And water'd heaven with their tears,
Did he smile his work to see?
Did he who made the Lamb make thee?

Tiger! Tiger! burning bright
In the forests of the night,
What immortal hand or eye,
Dare frame thy fearful symmetry?

—WILLIAM BLAKE

It would be an extraordinary person who has never given thought
to death—what it means and what final mystery it may reveal. The

poet often ponders this topic. Sometimes his feelings come from deep within himself and may or may not reflect a customary viewpoint. The next poem, by Sara Teasdale, speaks of this final mystery:

"THERE WILL BE REST"

> There will be rest, and sure stars shining
>   Over the roof-tops crowned with snow,
> A reign of rest, serene forgetting,
>   The music of stillness holy and low.
>
> I will make this world of my devising
>   Out of a dream in my lonely mind,
> I shall find the crystal of peace,—above me
>   Stars I shall find.

—SARA TEASDALE

Stephen Crane, in "The Blades of Grass," uses an interesting personification to express the idea that the best deeds are those done without thought of reward.

THE BLADES OF GRASS

> In Heaven,
> Some little blades of grass
> Stood before God.
> "What did you do?"
> Then all save one of the little blades
> Began eagerly to relate
> The merits of their lives.
> This one stayed a small way behind,
> Ashamed.
>
> Presently, God said,
> "And what did you do?"

The little blade answered, "Oh, my Lord,
Memory is bitter to me,
For, if I did good deeds,
I know not of them."
Then God, in all his splendor,
Arose from his throne.
"Oh, best little blade of grass!" he said.

—STEPHEN CRANE

Poets have many sources for their spiritual faith. Their beliefs may stem from an established church or religious sect; sometimes they originate from the poet's own experience and observation, and frequently they come from deep within the poet himself. Often poets express their most profound thoughts with great simplicity. An example of a poet who is famous for putting depth of feeling into remarkably short, clear verse is Emily Dickinson.

I NEVER SAW A MOOR

I never saw a moor,
I never saw the sea;
Yet know I how the heather looks,
And what a wave must be.

I never spoke with God,
Nor visited in Heaven;
Yet certain am I of the spot
As if the chart were given.

—EMILY DICKINSON

A poet whose beliefs were molded by his own painful life was William Ernest Henley, the author of the next poem. For nearly all his years he suffered from tuberculosis of the bone. His physical agony was intense and prolonged, and the death of his son added further tragedy to his life. From this distressing background came the noble poem "Invictus," considered by many people to be one of the finest expressions of personal courage ever made by man. The title means "unconquered."

INVICTUS

Out of the night that covers me,
    Black as the Pit from pole to pole,
I thank whatever gods may be
    For my unconquerable soul.

In the fell clutch of circumstance
    I have not winced nor cried aloud.
Under the bludgeonings of chance
    My head is bloody, but unbowed.

Beyond this place of wrath and tears
    Looms but the horror of the shade,
And yet the menace of the years
    Finds, and shall find me, unafraid.

It matters not how strait the gate,
    How charged with punishments the scroll,
I am the master of my fate:
    I am the captain of my soul.

—WILLIAM ERNEST HENLEY

The next poem is not an easy one to understand. It was written by Edwin Arlington Robinson, who, like W. E. Henley, lived a life full of pain and suffering. Robinson's pain was mental, of his own making, but it was nevertheless intense. The poem reflects this suffering and shows the poet groping for purpose and meaning in his stormy life. Its title, appropriately enough, means "I believe."

CREDO

I cannot find my way: there is no star
In all the shrouded heavens anywhere;
And there is not a whisper in the air
Of any living voice but one so far
That I can hear it only as a bar
Of lost, imperial music, played when fair
And angel fingers wove, and unaware,
Dead leaves to garlands where no roses are.

No, there is not a glimmer, nor a call,
For one that welcomes, welcomes when he fears,
The black and awful chaos of the night;
But through it all—above, beyond it all—
I know the far-sent message of the years,
I feel the coming glory of the Light!

—EDWIN ARLINGTON ROBINSON

The next selection is a short portion from a much longer poem. These lines contain some of the conclusions about the meaning of life that the poet, Edna St. Vincent Millay, reached after much thought. As you study the poem compare its ideas with those of "Credo." You will find some similarities, but you will also discover some vast differences.

RENASCENCE

* * * * * * *

The world stands out on either side
No wider than the heart is wide;
Above the world is stretched the sky,—
No higher than the soul is high.

The heart can push the sea and land
Farther away on either hand;
The soul can split the sky in two,
And let the face of God shine through.
But East and West will pinch the heart
That can not keep them pushed apart;
And he whose soul is flat—the sky
Will cave in on him by and by.

—EDNA ST. VINCENT MILLAY

The religious literature of the major faiths is not customarily thought of as *poetry;* but it is indeed very poetic in feeling and words, as the next selections will show. Notice, as you read the various excerpts, the richness and beauty of their metaphorical language.

PSALM 23

The Lord is my shepherd; I shall not want.

He maketh me to lie down in green pastures: he leadeth me beside the still waters.

He restoreth my soul: he leadeth me in the paths of righteousness for his name's sake.

Yea, though I walk through the valley of the shadow of death, I will fear no evil: for thou art with me; thy rod and thy staff they comfort me.

Thou preparest a table before me in the presence of mine enemies: thou anointest my head with oil; my cup runneth over.

Surely goodness and mercy shall follow me all the days of my life: and I will dwell in the house of the Lord for ever.

—*from* THE KING JAMES BIBLE

ECCLESIASTES

from CHAPTER 3

All things have their season, and in their times all things pass under heaven.

A time to be born and a time to die. A time to plant, and a time to pluck up that which is planted.

A time to kill, and a time to heal. A time to destroy, and a time to build.

A time to weep, and a time to laugh. A time to mourn, and a time to dance.

A time to scatter stones, and a time to gather. A time to embrace, and a time to be far from embraces.

A time to get, and a time to lose. A time to keep, and a time to cast away.

A time to rend, and a time to sew. A time to keep silence, and a time to speak.

A time of love, and a time of hatred. A time of war, and a time of peace.

*   *   *   *   *   *   *

—*from* THE DOUAY BIBLE

GENESIS

from CHAPTER 1

In the beginning God created the heaven and the earth. Now the earth was unformed and void, and darkness was upon the face of the deep; and the spirit of God hovered over the face of the waters. And God said: "Let there be light." And there was light. And God saw the light, that it was good; and God divided the light from the darkness. And God called the light Day, and the darkness He called Night. And there was evening and there was morning, one day.

—*from* THE HOLY SCRIPTURES

RUTH

from CHAPTER 1

    And Ruth said, Intreat me not to leave thee, or to return from following after thee: for whither thou goest, I will go; and where thou lodgest, I will lodge: thy people shall be my people, and thy God my God:

    Where thou diest, will I die, and there will I be buried: the Lord do so to me, and more also, if aught but death part thee and me.

                            —*from* THE KING JAMES BIBLE

ISAIAS

from CHAPTER 35

    The land that was desolate and impassable shall be glad, and the wilderness shall rejoice, and shall flourish like the lily.

    It shall bud forth and blossom, and shall rejoice with joy and praise: the glory of Libanus is given to it: the beauty of Carmel, and Saron, they shall see the glory of the Lord, and the beauty of our God.

    Strengthen ye the feeble hands, and confirm the weak knees.

    Say to the fainthearted: Take courage, and fear not: behold your God will bring the revenge of recompense: God himself will come and will save you.

    Then shall the eyes of the blind be opened, and the ears of the deaf shall be unstopped.

    Then shall the lame man leap as a hart, and the tongue of the dumb shall be free: for waters are broken out in the desert, and streams in the wilderness.

    And that which was dry land, shall become a pool, and the thirsty land springs of water. In the dens where dragons dwelt before, shall rise up the verdure of the reed and the bulrush.

               —*from* THE HOLY BIBLE, CONFRATERNITY EDITION

JOB

For there is hope of a tree,
If it be cut down, that it will sprout again,
And that the tender branch thereof will not cease.
Though the root thereof wax old in the earth,
And the stock thereof die in the ground;
Yet through the scent of water it will bud,
And put forth boughs like a plant.
But man dieth, and lieth low;
Yea, man perisheth, and where is he?
As the waters fail from the sea,
And the river is drained dry;
So man lieth down and riseth not; ·
Till the heavens be no more, they shall not awake,
Nor be roused out of their sleep.

—*from* THE HOLY SCRIPTURES

Last of these poems of faith is Mark Van Doren's "The God of Galaxies." As science continues to push outward the boundaries of the universe, man finds his own planet becoming a smaller and smaller speck in the great picture. This poem expresses the poet's belief that we must expand our idea of God to include all creation, to realize that the power behind the universe is as great and profound as the cosmos itself.

THE GOD OF GALAXIES

The god of galaxies has more to govern
Than the first men imagined, when one mountain
Trumpeted his anger, and one rainbow,
Red in the east, restored them to his love.

One earth it was, with big and lesser torches,
And stars by night for candles. And he spoke
To single persons, sitting in their tents.

Now streams of worlds, now powdery great whirlwinds
Of universes far enough away
To seem but fog-wisps in a bank of night
So measureless the mind can sicken, trying—
Now seas of darkness, shoreless, on and on
Encircled by themselves, yet washing farther
Than the last triple sun, revolving, shows.

The god of galaxies—how shall we praise him?
For on we must, or wither. Yet what word
Of words? And where to send it, on which night
Of winter stars, of summer, or by autumn
In the first evening of the Pleiades?
The god of galaxies, of burning gases,
May have forgotten Leo and the Bull.

But God remembers, and is everywhere.
He even is the void, where nothing shines.
He is the absence of his own reflection
In the deep gulf; he is the dusky cinder
Of pure fire in its prime; he is the place
Prepared for hugest planets: black idea,
Brooding between fierce poles he keeps apart.

Those altitudes and oceans, though, with islands
Drifting, blown immense as by a wind,
And yet no wind; and not one blazing coast
Where thought could live, could listen—oh, what word
Of words? Let us consider it in terror,
And say it without voice. Praise universes
Numberless. Praise all of them. Praise Him.

—MARK VAN DOREN

1. "Some Keep the Sabbath" gives several substitutes that the poet preferred in place of customary church services. List a few of her substitutes.

2. What do you feel Miss Dickinson meant in the last two lines of this poem?

3. In "My Heart Leaps Up" does the "rainbow" stand for things other than itself? What do you think it symbolizes?

4. What do you think Wordsworth means by this statement?

   The Child is father of the Man;

5. What does Miss Millay find in "God's World" that thrills her so?

6. What does Miss Millay mean in the last two lines of the poem when she says, "let fall no burning leaf; prithee, let no bird call"?

7. Why did the poet choose to place a capital letter on "Someone" in the last stanza of "All But Blind"?

8. Walter de la Mare uses very short lines in this poem. Do you feel the poem is more effective this way than it might have been with longer lines? Explain your reaction.

9. What is the "one fierce hour" of which the donkey speaks?

10. The first four lines of "The Donkey" seem very unusual. Explain what you think the poet was trying to say in them.

11. What does William Blake seem to be saying in "The Tiger" when he asks, "Did he who made the Lamb make thee"?

12. There have been some people who have insisted that "The Tiger" is so beautifully written that its meaning is unimportant; that is, it matters little to the reader, they say, whether the poem can be understood or not. Would you agree or disagree with this idea? Explain.

13. In Sara Teasdale's "There Will be Rest," she mentions the "sure stars," "the rooftops crowned with snow," and the "music of stillness." How do these ideas fit in with her title?

14. Why do you think Miss Teasdale longs so for rest?

15. What do you believe the "blades of grass" stand for in Stephen Crane's poem?

16. What qualities does the "little blade of grass" show that make it "best" of all?

17. "I Never Saw a Moor" illustrates several of Miss Dickinson's characteristics, both as a poet and as a woman of deep faith. What are some of these qualities?

18. When Miss Dickinson first wrote the poem, she used the words "and what a billow be" in place of "and what a wave must be." In your judgment, which was the better line? Explain.

19. Henley's "Invictus" is a reflection of his own experience. Find several illustrations in the poem that seem to be taken from his own unfortunate life.

20. It has been said that if Henley had never written more than the last two lines of the poem, his name in poetry would still be known today. What do these lines mean to you?

21. What do you think Edwin Arlington Robinson meant with "there is no star"?

22. Interpret the lines:

> For one that welcomes, welcomes when he fears,
> The black and awful chaos of the night.

23. What does Miss Millay mean in her poem "Renascence" by these lines?

> But East and West will pinch the heart
> That cannot keep them pushed apart.

24. In what ways do the ideas presented in "Renascence" differ from those of "Credo"?

25. In "The God of Galaxies" does Mark Van Doren's own belief in a supreme being seem strong or weak? Explain.

26. How is this poem appropriate as a conclusion to this chapter?

CHAPTER SEVEN

Humor

A great many poems are written just for fun. In this chapter you will find a few of the thousands of humorous poems that exist in English. Some of the verses make fun of well-known things; some laugh at people who are too serious; some are just nonsense, to be enjoyed for their own sake. In serious poetry you often must look deeply into the poems to discover the writers' more profound thoughts and ideas; in humorous verse, all that is asked of you is that you enjoy what you find amusing. There are poems that will make you laugh aloud, and others that will provoke an inner chuckle. But in whatever size or shape your laughter comes, the important thing is that it comes.

Limericks are humorous verses that always have the same length and form. In Chapter Eleven you will find directions for writing your own. For the moment, here are a few to enjoy:

I remember a fellow named Louie,
Who ate seventeen bowls of chop-suey;
When the eighteenth was brought,
He became overwrought,
And we watched as poor Louie went blooie!

—ANONYMOUS

A lady from near Lake Louise
Declared she was bothered by fleas.
She used gasoline
And later was seen
Sailing over the hills and the trees.

—ANONYMOUS

There was an old grouch from Ontario
Who purchased a thousand-watt stereo.
When he turned it up loud
He collected a crowd
And they strangled him with his own aerial.

—ANONYMOUS

A man hired by John Smith and Co.
Loudly declared that he'd tho.
    Men that he saw
    Dumping dirt near his store.
The drivers, therefore, didn't do.

          —MARK TWAIN

The pattern of the limerick is so well-known that the following poem gains its humor by varying the usual forms:

There was a young man of Spokane
Whose verses never would scan.
    When told it was so,
    He said, "Yes, I know,
But I always try to get as many words in the
    last line as I possibly can."

          —ANONYMOUS

Sometimes the humor of a poem is partially based on its being written in dialect; that is, it uses the regional form of a language, or the speech of someone who speaks so-called "broken English," or who is careless of his diction. Here are a few dialect poems.

MIA CARLOTTA

Giuseppe, da barber, ees greata for "mash,"
He gotta da bigga, da blacka mustache,
Good clo'es an' good styla an' playnta good cash.

W'enevra Giuseppe ees walk on da street,
Da people dey talka, "how nobby! how neat!
How softa da handa, how smalla da feet."

He leefta hees hat an' he shaka hees curls,
An' smila weeth teetha so shiny like pearls;
O! manny da heart of da seely young girls

He gotta.
Yes, playnta he gotta—
But notta
Carlotta!

Giuseppe, da barber, he maka da eye,
An' lika da steam engine puffa an' sigh,
For catcha Carlotta w'en she ees go by.

Carlotta she walka weeth nose in da air,
An' look through Giuseppe weeth far-away stare,
As eef she no see dere ees som'body dere.

Giuseppe, da barber, he gotta da cash,
He gotta da clo'es an' da bigga mustache,
He gotta da seely young girls for da "mash,"
But notta—
You bat my life, notta—
Carlotta.
I gotta!

—T. A. DALY

BETWEEN TWO LOVES

I gotta love for Angela,
I love Carlotta, too.
I no can marry both o' dem,
So w'at I gona do?

O! Angela ees pretta girl,
She gotta hair so black, so curl,
An' teeth so white as anytheeng.
An' oh, she gotta voice to seeng,
Dat mak' your hearta feel eet must
Jomp up an' dance or eet weell bust.

An' alla time she seeng, her eyes
Dey smila like Italia's skies,
An' makin' flirtin' looks at you—
But dat ees all w'at she can do.

Carlotta ees no gotta song,
But she ees twice so big an' strong
As Angela, an' she no look
So beautiful—but she can cook.
You oughta see her carry wood!
I tal you w'at, eet do you good.
When she ees be som'body's wife
She worka hard, you bat my life!
She nevva gattin' tired, too—
But dat ees all w'at she can do.

Oh, my! I weesh dat Angela
    Was strong for carry wood,
Or else Carlotta gotta song
    An' looka pretta good.
I gotta love for Angela,
    I love Carlotta, too.
I no can marry both o' dem,
    So w'at I gona do?   —T. A. DALY

UNCLE SIMON AND UNCLE JIM

Uncle Simon he
Clumb up a tree
To see
What he could see,
When presentlee
Uncle Jim
Clumb up beside of him
And squatted down by he.

—CHARLES FARRAR BROWNE (ARTEMUS WARD)

TO BE OR NOT TO BE

I

I sometimes think I'd rather crow
And be a rooster than to roost
And be a crow. But I dunno.

II

A rooster he can roost also,
Which don't seem fair when crows can't crow.
Which may help some. Still I dunno.

III

Crows should be glad of one thing, though;
Nobody thinks of eating crow,
While roosters they are good enough
For anyone unless they're tough.

IV

There are lots of tough old roosters, though,
And anyway a crow can't crow,
So mebby roosters stand more show.
It looks that way. But I dunno.

—ANONYMOUS

Poets occasionally become intrigued with words and letters, or with the strange irregularities of our language. Here are two tricky verses that might give you some ideas for your own compositions.

LOGIC

I have a copper penny and another copper penny,
  Well, then, of course, I have two copper pence;
I have a cousin Jenny and another cousin Jenny,
  Well, pray, then, do I have two cousin Jence?

—ANONYMOUS

SUSAN SIMPSON

Sudden swallows swiftly skimming,
    Sunset's slowly spreading shade,
Silvery songsters sweetly singing,
    Summer's soothing serenade.

Susan Simpson strolled sedately,
    Stifling sobs, suppressing sighs.
Seeing Stephen Slocum, stately
    She stopped, showing some surprise.

"Say," said Stephen, "sweetest sigher;
    Say, shall Stephen spouseless stay?"
Susan, seeming somewhat shyer,
    Showed submissiveness straightway.

Summer's season slowly stretches,
    Susan Simpson Slocum she—
So she signed some simple sketches—
    Soul sought soul successfully.

*   *   *   *   *   *   *

Six Septembers Susan swelters;
    Six sharp seasons snow supplied;
Susan's satin sofa shelters
    Six small Slocums side by side.

—ANONYMOUS

Often writers with a sense of humor like to play with words and ideas, even though the results don't seem to mean very much. This type of writing is called "nonsense" when it has little or no significance beyond the funny ideas presented, and "whimsey" when the poet lets his humorous imagination guide him. Here are some samples of nonsense and whimsey.

JABBERWOCKY

'Twas brillig, and the slithy toves
   Did gyre and gimble in the wabe;
All mimsy were the borogoves,
   And the mome raths outgrabe.

"Beware the Jabberwock, my son!
   The jaws that bite, the claws that catch!
Beware the Jubjub bird, and shun
   The frumious Bandersnatch!"

He took his vorpal sword in hand:
   Long time the manxome foe he sought.
So rested he by the Tumtum tree,
   And stood awhile in thought.

And as in uffish thought he stood,
   The Jabberwock with eyes of flame,
Came whiffling through the tulgey wood,
   And burbled as it came!

One, two! One, two! And through, and through
   The vorpal blade went snicker-snack!
He left it dead, and with its head
   He went galumphing back.

"And hast thou slain the Jabberwock?
   Come to my arms, my beamish boy!
Oh, frabjous day! Callooh! callay!"
   He chortled in his joy.

'Twas brillig, and the slithy toves
   Did gyre and gimble in the wabe;
All mimsy were the borogoves
   And the mome raths outgrabe.

—LEWIS CARROLL

"You are old, Father William," the young man said,
  "And your hair has become very white;
And yet you incessantly stand on your head—
  Do you think, at your age, it is right?"

"In my youth," Father William replied to his son,
  "I feared it might injure the brain;
But now that I'm perfectly sure I have none,
  Why, I do it again and again."

"You are old," said the youth, "as I mentioned before,
  And have grown most uncommonly fat;
Yet you turned a back somersault in at the door—
  Pray, what is the reason of that?"

"In my youth," said the sage, as he shook his gray locks,
  "I kept all my limbs very supple
By the use of this ointment—one shilling the box—
  Allow me to sell you a couple."

"You are old," said the youth, "and your jaws are too weak
  For anything tougher than suet;
Yet you finished the goose, with the bones and the beak;
  Pray, how did you manage to do it?"

"In my youth," said his father, "I took to the law,
  And argued each case with my wife;
And the muscular strength which it gave to my jaw,
  Has lasted the rest of my life."

"You are old," said the youth; "one would hardly suppose
  That your eye was as steady as ever;
Yet you balanced an eel on the end of your nose—
  What made you so awfully clever?"

"I have answered three questions, and that is enough,"
    Said his father; "don't give yourself airs!
Do you think I can listen all day to such stuff?
    Be off, or I'll kick you down-stairs!"

—LEWIS CARROLL

THE PURPLE COW

I never saw a Purple Cow,
    I never hope to see one;
But I can tell you, anyhow,
    I'd rather see than be one.

—GELETT BURGESS

THE LAZY ROOF

The Roof it has a Lazy Time
    A-lying in the Sun;
The Walls they have to Hold Him Up
    They do Not Have Much Fun!

—GELETT BURGESS

MY FEET

My Feet, they haul me Round the House,
    They Hoist me up the Stairs;
I only have to Steer them and
    They Ride me Everywheres.

—GELETT BURGESS

Animals seem to be favorite subjects for humorous poems. Here is a set of such poems in which the writers have fun with the animal kingdom and, indirectly, with human beings, too.

THE RHINOCEROS

The rhino is a homely beast,
For human eyes he's not a feast.
Farewell, farewell, you old rhinoceros,
I'll stare at something less prepoceros!

—OGDEN NASH

THE PANTHER

The panther is like a leopard,
Except it hasn't been peppered.
Should you behold a panther crouch,
Prepare to say Ouch.
Better yet, if called by a panther,
Don't anther.

—OGDEN NASH

UNSATISFIED YEARNING

Down in the silent hallway
Scampers the dog about,
And whines, and barks, and scratches,
In order to get out.

Once in the glittering starlight,
He straightway doth begin
To set up a doleful howling
In order to get in.

—RICHARD KENDALL MUNKITTRICK

THE MICROBE

The Microbe is so very small
You cannot make him out at all,
But many sanguine people hope
To see him through a microscope.
His jointed tongue that lies beneath
A hundred curious rows of teeth;
His seven tufted tails with lots
Of lovely pink and purple spots,
On each of which a pattern stands,
Composed of forty separate bands;
His eyebrows of a tender green;
All these have never yet been seen—
But Scientists, who ought to know,
Assure us that they must be so. . . .
Oh! let us never, never doubt
What nobody is sure about!

—HILAIRE BELLOC

THE PLAINT OF THE CAMEL

"Canary birds feed on sugar and seed,
  Parrots have crackers to crunch;
And as for the poodles, they tell me the noodles
  Have chickens and cream for their lunch.
    But there's never a question
    About *my* digestion—
  Anything does for me!

"Cats, you're aware, can repose in a chair,
  Chickens can roost upon rails;
Puppies are able to sleep in a stable,
  And oysters can slumber in pails.

But no one supposes
A poor Camel dozes—
Any place does for me!

"Lambs are enclosed where it's never exposed.
  Coops are constructed for hens;
Kittens are treated to houses well heated,
  And pigs are protected by pens.
    But a Camel comes handy
    Wherever it's sandy—
Anywhere does for me!

"People would laugh if you rode a giraffe,
  Or mounted the back of an ox;
It's nobody's habit to ride on a rabbit,
  Or try to bestraddle a fox.
    But as for a Camel, he's
    Ridden by families—
Any load does for me!

"A snake is as round as a hole in the ground,
  And weasels are wavy and sleek;
And no alligator could ever be straighter
  Than lizards that live in a creek,
But a Camel's all lumpy
    And bumpy and humpy—
Any shape does for me!"

—CHARLES EDWARD CARRYL

THE VIPER

Yet another great truth I record in my verse,
That some Vipers are venomous, some the reverse;

A fact you may prove if you try,
By procuring two Vipers and letting them bite;
With the *first* you are only the worse for a fright,
But after the *second* you die.

—HILAIRE BELLOC

HOW TO TELL THE WILD ANIMALS

If ever you should go by chance
    To jungles in the East;
And if there should to you advance
    A large and tawny beast,
If he roars at you as you're dyin'
    You'll know it is the Asian Lion.

Or if some time when roaming round,
    A noble wild beast greets you,
With black stripes on a yellow ground,
    Just notice if he eats you.
This simple rule may help you learn
    The Bengal Tiger to discern.

If strolling forth, a beast you view,
    Whose hide with spots is peppered,
As soon as he has lept on you
    You'll know it is the Leopard.
'Twill do no good to roar with pain,
    He'll only lep and lep again.

If when you're walking round your yard,
    You meet a creature there,
Who hugs you very, very hard,
    Be sure it is the Bear.
If you have any doubt, I guess
    He'll give you just one more caress.

Though to distinguish beasts of prey
    A novice might nonplus,
The Crocodiles you always may
    Tell from Hyenas thus:
Hyenas come with merry smiles;
    But if they weep, they're Crocodiles.

The true Chameleon is small,
    A lizard sort of thing;
He hasn't any ears at all,
    And not a single wing.
If there is nothing on the tree,
    'Tis the Chameleon you see.

—CAROLYN WELLS

THE RHYME
OF THE CHIVALROUS SHARK

Most chivalrous fish of the ocean,
    To ladies forbearing and mild,
Though his record be dark, is the man-eating shark,
    Who will eat neither woman nor child.

He dines upon seamen and skippers,
    And tourists his hunger assuage,
And a fresh cabin boy will inspire him with joy
    If he's past the maturity age.

A doctor, a lawyer, a preacher,
    He'll gobble one any fine day,
But the ladies, God bless 'em, he'll only address 'em
    Politely and go on his way.

I can readily cite you an instance
     Where a lovely young lady of Breem,
Who was tender and sweet and delicious to eat,
     Fell into the bay with a scream.

She struggled and flounced in the water,
     And signaled in vain for her bark,
And she'd surely been drowned if she hadn't been found
     By the chivalrous man-eating shark.

He bowed in a manner most polished,
     Thus soothing her impulses wild;
"Don't be frightened," he said, "I've been properly bred
     And will eat neither woman nor child."

Then he proffered his fin and she took it—
     Such a gallantry none can dispute—
While the passengers cheered as the vessel they neared
     And a broadside was fired in salute.

And they soon stood alongside the vessel,
     When a life-saving dinghy was lowered
With the pick of the crew, and her relatives, too,
     And the mate and the skipper aboard.

So they took her aboard in a jiffy,
     And the shark stood attention the while,
Then he raised on his flipper and ate up the skipper
     And went on his way with a smile.

And this shows that the prince of the ocean,
     To ladies forbearing and mild,
Though his record be dark, is the man-eating shark,
     Who will eat neither woman nor child.

                                        —WALLACE IRWIN

Many young people go through a period in their lives when they make fun of the old established values and beliefs that have been handed down to them. Perhaps you have acquaintances who even pretend to sneer at the sincerity of their fellow human beings and to be sarcastic about ideas which you, yourself, hold to be true. Such people are said to be "cynical"; that is, they ridicule many things by seeming to "know better." Fortunately, most such young cynics outgrow this attitude and learn to be more tolerant and good-humored as they find that there are true values and good will in the world. Samuel Hoffenstein, in the next poem, adopts an amusingly cynical attitude. He emphasizes the negative side of his subject, thus making life seem rather hopeless and hardly worth the trouble, but you will see that his cynicism has a light touch, and that he does not take his point of view very seriously.

from POEMS IN PRAISE
OF PRACTICALLY NOTHING

I

You buy some flowers for your table;
You tend them tenderly as you're able;
You fetch them water from hither and thither—
What thanks do you get for it all? They wither.

IV

You buy yourself a new suit of clothes;
The care you give it, God only knows;
The material, of course, is the very *best* yet;
You get it pressed and pressed and *pressed* yet;
You keep it free from specks so tiny—
What thanks do you get? The pants get shiny.

You're a positive fiend for life extension:
You eat greens in every dimension;
You know as well as any parrot
The quirks of calory and carrot—
They've taken out, without a quiver,
Your tonsils, teeth, ambition, liver,
Appendix, income—every center
Designed to let bacilli enter.
You never miss the daily dozen
That killed your uncle, brother, cousin;
You breathe only the freshest breezes—
And what do you get? The same diseases.

—SAMUEL HOFFENSTEIN

Poets are very much aware of the world around them and of the shortcomings of the people who live in it. Often they criticize what they observe, sometimes bitterly. When they hold up for examination some attitude or idea that they feel is wrong and should be corrected, they frequently use a device known as "satire." Satire is a form of criticism in which a subject is treated with humorous disrespect. The writer may simply smile gently as he describes the peculiarities of people and their strange ways; at the opposite extreme, he may attack with a savage grin something he feels is evil and must be changed. Always, however, satire is meant to be amusing, although it is not always "funny." By using such techniques as sarcasm, irony, and exaggeration (terms you may want to look up), the writer makes the object of his criticism seem ridiculously shallow or blind or foolish. The good satirist never says, "Look! I disapprove of this." By carefully emphasizing its own flaws, he lets the subject of his attack condemn itself. This is well illustrated in the second of the following poems.

The next two selections are examples of rather gentle satire. Ogden Nash smiles at one element in human nature that causes unhappiness in many people. W. S. Gilbert laughs more sharply at a quality which you may find annoying in some of your acquaintances. Both poems are satirical; they criticize in an amusing way without ever saying, "This is a criticism."

KINDLY UNHITCH THAT STAR, BUDDY

I hardly suppose I know anybody who wouldn't rather be a success
      than a failure,
Just as I suppose every piece of crabgrass in the garden would much
      rather be an azalea,
And in celestial circles all the run-of-the-mill angels would rather be
      archangels or at least cherubim and seraphim,
And in the legal world all the little process-servers hope to grow up
      into great big bailiffim and sheriffim.
Indeed, everybody wants to be a wow,
But not everybody knows exactly how.
Some people think they will eventually wear diamonds instead of
      rhinestones
Only by everlastingly keeping their noses to their ghrinestones,
And other people think they will be able to put in more time at Palm
      Beach and the Ritz
By not paying too much attention to attendance at the office but
      rather in being brilliant by starts and fits.
Some people after a full day's work sit up all night getting a college
      education by correspondence,
While others seem to think they'll get just as far by devoting their
      evenings to the study of the difference in temperament between
      brunettance and blondance.
In short, the world is filled with people trying to achieve success,
And half of them think they'll get it by saying No and half of them
      by saying Yes,

And if all the ones who say No said Yes, and vice versa, such is the
    fate of humanity that ninety-nine per cent of them still wouldn't
    be any better off than they were before,
Which perhaps is just as well because if everybody was a success
    nobody could be contemptuous of anybody else and everybody
    would start in all over again trying to be a bigger success than
    everybody else so they would have somebody to be contemptu-
    ous of and so on forevermore,
Because when people start hitching their wagons to a star,
That's the way they are.

—OGDEN NASH

THE DISAGREEABLE MAN

If you give me your attention, I will tell you what I am:
I'm a genuine philanthropist—all other kinds are sham.
Each little fault of temper and each social defect
In my erring fellow-creatures, I endeavor to correct.
To all their little weaknesses I open peoples' eyes,
And little plans to snub the self-sufficient I devise;
I love my fellow-creatures—I do all the good I can—
Yet everybody says I'm such a disagreeable man!
        And I can't think why!

To compliments inflated I've a withering reply,
And vanity I always do my best to mortify;
A charitable action I can skillfully dissect;
And interested motives I'm delighted to detect.
I know everybody's income and what everybody earns,
And I carefully compare it with the income-tax returns;
But to benefit humanity, however much I plan,
Yet everybody says I'm such a disagreeable man!
        And I can't think why!

I'm sure I'm no ascetic; I'm as pleasant as can be;
You'll always find me ready with a crushing repartee;
I've an irritating chuckle, I've a celebrated sneer,
I've an entertaining snigger, I've a fascinating leer;
To everybody's prejudice I know a thing or two;
I can tell a woman's age in half a minute—and I do—
But although I try to make myself as pleasant as I can,
Yet everybody says I'm such a disagreeable man!
              And I can't think why!

                            —W. S. GILBERT

Occasionally poets like to play with the language just for the fun of it. The final two poems in this chapter are examples of word-play; perhaps they will tempt you to try writing a poem of this ingenious sort.

AMBIGUOUS LINES

read with a comma after the first noun in each line

I saw a peacock with a fiery tail
I saw a blazing comet pour down hail
I saw a cloud all wrapt with ivy round
I saw a lofty oak creep on the ground
I saw a beetle swallow up a whale
I saw a foaming sea brimful of ale
I saw a pewter cup sixteen feet deep
I saw a well full of men's tears that weep
I saw wet eyes in flames of living fire
I saw a house as high as the moon and higher
I saw the glorious sun at deep midnight
I saw the man who saw this wondrous sight.

I saw a pack of cards gnawing a bone
I saw a dog seated on Britain's throne
I saw King George shut up within a box
I saw an orange driving a fat ox
I saw a butcher not a twelvemonth old
I saw a great-coat all of solid gold
I saw two buttons telling of their dreams
I saw my friends who wished I'd quit these themes.

—UNKNOWN

N O !

No sun—no moon!
No morn—no noon—
No dawn—no dusk—no proper time of day—
No sky—no earthly view—
No distance looking blue—
No road—no street—no "t'other side the way"—
No end to any Row—
No indications where the Crescents go—
No top to any steeple—
No recognitions of familiar people—
No courtesies for showing 'em—
No knowing 'em!
No travelling at all—no locomotion,
No inkling of the way—no notion—
"No go"—by land or ocean—
No mail—no post—
No news from any foreign coast—
No park—no ring—no afternoon gentility—
No company—no nobility—
No warmth, no cheerfulness, no healthful ease,

No comfortable feel in any member—
No shade, no shine, no butterflies, no bees,
No fruits, no flowers, no leaves, no birds,
November!

—THOMAS HOOD

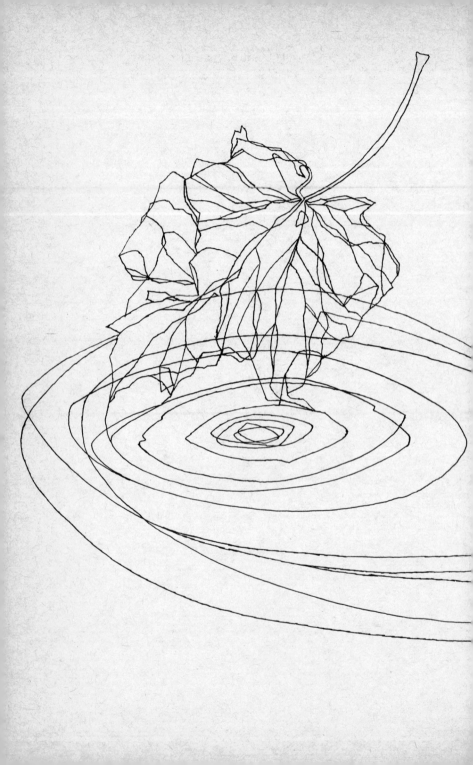

CHAPTER EIGHT

Reflections

There are many poems in our language that reflect the moods and thoughtful moments that everyone has. Young people even more than older people are subject to a wide variety of moods—sometimes joyful, sometimes sad, sometimes inward-looking. These feelings may be brought on by an event or the weather or a song on the radio; they may even occur as an outgrowth of the way someone happens to be feeling.

The thoughts that grow out of these moods are often serious ones. Loneliness, for example, may trouble you from time to time, and you find yourself trying to work out in your mind your relationship to others. There are occasions when you may be overwhelmed by all the little duties of everyday living, and you may wonder why it is that you always seem to be so busy, why you don't have time to stop and think. A death in the family may make you ponder the old question of the meaning of life. On the other hand, many moods are not so solemn; one day you may suddenly feel wanderlust, the desire to get away from it all; or you may get up one morning feeling that everything is just as it should be, and that the day will surely be a happy one. All these feelings are a combination of outward and inward influences, often too complicated to explain but always very real.

The poetry in this chapter reflects many moods, and it explores some of the thoughts that often go along with them. Several of the poems may cause you to reflect upon things you perhaps haven't yet had time to think about very much. Do not be surprised, however, if you find that most of the poems describe moods that you have already felt and thought about, but have never put clearly into words.

As you read the first poem, you may feel that the speaker is like a customer at Christmas time, overladen with many packages. This thought is only a part of the poem, however; there is more here than an armful of parcels.

THE ARMFUL

For every parcel I stoop down to seize,
I lose some other off my arms and knees,

And the whole pile is slipping, bottles, buns,
Extremes too hard to comprehend at once,
Yet nothing I should care to leave behind.
With all I have to hold with, hand and mind
And heart, if need be, I will do my best
To keep their building balanced at my breast.
I crouch down to prevent them as they fall;
Then sit down in the middle of them all.
I had to drop the armful in the road
And try to stack them in a better load.

—ROBERT FROST

More than one hundred and fifty years ago, one of the best-known poets, William Wordsworth, felt some of the same pressures that many people are aware of today, pressures that make them stop and wonder about their overly-busy lives.

THE WORLD IS TOO MUCH WITH US

The world is too much with us; late and soon,
Getting and spending, we lay waste our powers:
Little we see in Nature that is ours;
We have given our hearts away, a sordid boon!
The Sea that bares her bosom to the moon;
The winds that will be howling at all hours,
And are up-gathered now like sleeping flowers;
For this, for everything, we are out of tune;
It moves us not.—Great God! I'd rather be
A Pagan suckled in a creed outworn;
So might I, standing on this pleasant lea,
Have glimpses that would make me less forlorn;
Have sight of Proteus rising from the sea;
Or hear old Triton blow his wreathéd horn.

—WILLIAM WORDSWORTH

Sometimes you may realize, as did William Wordsworth in the poem you have just read, that people can create enormous problems for themselves—problems that do not *need* to exist but nevertheless do exist. Part of the difficulty, perhaps, stems from man's superior intelligence that seems to drive him toward goals impossible to achieve. Have you ever envied a pet that—untroubled by the intelligence that enriches yet distresses man—seems utterly content?

DOG

O little friend, your nose is ready; you sniff,
Asking for that expected walk,
(Your nostrils full of the happy rabbit-whiff)
And almost talk.

And so the moment becomes a moving force;
Coats glide down from their pegs in the humble dark;
You scamper the stairs,
Your body informed with the scent and the track and the mark
Of stoats and weasels, moles and badgers and hares.

We are going *Out*. You know the pitch of the word,
Probing the tone of thought as it comes through fog
And reaches by devious means (half-smelt, half-heard)
The four-legged brain of a walk-ecstatic dog.

Out through the garden your head is already low.
You are going your walk, you know,
And your limbs will draw
Joy from the earth through the touch of your padded paw.

Now, sending a look to us behind,
Who follow slowly the track of your lovely play,
You fetch our bodies forward away from mind
Into the light and fun of your useless day.

* * * * * * *

Thus, for your walk, we took ourselves, and went
Out by the hedge, and tree, to the open ground.
You ran, in delightful strata of wafted scent,
Over the hill without seeing the view;
Beauty is hinted through primitive smells to you:
And that ultimate Beauty you track is but rarely found.

* * * * * * *

Home . . . and further joy will be waiting there:
Supper full of the lovely taste of bone,
You lift up your nose again, and sniff, and stare
For the rapture known
Of the quick wild gorge of food, then the still lie-down;
While your people will talk above you in the light
Of candles, and your dreams will merge and drown
Into the bed-delicious hours of night.

—HAROLD MONRO

Getting into a rut and losing your sense of what is important or unimportant are two pitfalls that you will always be struggling to avoid. Peggy Bacon looked at this problem from an unusual viewpoint.

COBBLER

He mends the shoes
and watches the feet
of the crowd that goes
along the street.

A basement deep
and a sidewalk high;
along the ceiling
the feet go by;

toeing and heeling
they seem to skim
the top of the larky
world to him

in the musty dark,
whose eyes dilate
as he gazes up
through the dingy grate.

The world hobbles
on feet of clay,
the cobbler cobbles
his days away;

crooked heels
and broken toes
are all he feels,
all he knows.   —PEGGY BACON

The cobbler let himself become so narrow in his outlook that he lost sight of the more meaningful things in life. Man often yearns for something beyond the everyday drudgery of existence. In the next poem a coal miner speaks:

CALIBAN IN THE COAL MINES

God, we don't like to complain.
　　We know that the mine is no lark.
But—there's the pools from the rain;
　　But—there's the cold and the dark.

God, You don't know what it is—
　　You, in Your well-lighted sky—
Watching the meteors whizz;
　　Warm, with a sun always by.

God, if You had but the moon
    Stuck in Your cap for a lamp,
Even You'd tire of it soon,
    Down in the dark and the damp.

Nothing but blackness above
    And nothing that moves but the cars. . . .
God, if You wish for our love,
    Fling us a handful of stars!

                —LOUIS UNTERMEYER

Have you ever tried to decide what you would consider the most important thing in all creation? Paul Engle arrived at his conclusion in the following unusual poem.

CAT'S EYE

                If suddenly blackness crawled
Over the world and the sun hurtled down
The vast and verge of space until it glowed
No bigger than a cat's eye in the night,
And wind beat the bruised face of the earth with awful
Tornado-clubbing fists, and all the waters
Rose in a leaping body to the heavens
Tidally challenging the moon, and then
With foaming, gibbering mouth went howling over
The shuddering plains and ocean bottoms:
                      If stars
Splattered and dashed the sky, and the moon wallowed
Dark without the sun, and I were the last
Man moving through the streets of towns the tiny
Pale hands of men had fashioned, and out of the shouting
Air and split space and trembling earth a voice
Asked softly what one thing I wished to see

Before the universe grew tense and cracked
To the core, and burst beyond the farthest gaunt
Galaxies of heaven, I would plead
That through the shadow there would loom the friendly
White magnificence of a human face.

—PAUL ENGLE

Moods have a way of changing—serious thoughts usually give way to lighter ones. The call of distant places can be very loud sometimes, when life seems to grow monotonous.

The next three poems are based on the theme of wanderlust—the thirst to see new places, to widen one's life. You have doubtless felt it already and will feel it many times through the years.

TRAVEL

The railroad track is miles away,
    And the day is loud with voices speaking,
Yet there isn't a train goes by all day
    But I hear its whistle shrieking.

All night there isn't a train goes by,
    Though the night is still for sleep and dreaming,
But I see its cinders red on the sky,
    And hear its engine steaming.

My heart is warm with the friends I make,
    And better friends I'll not be knowing;
Yet there isn't a train I wouldn't take,
    No matter where it's going.

—EDNA ST. VINCENT MILLAY

SEA GYPSY

I am fevered with the sunset,
I am fretful with the bay,
For the wander-thirst is on me
And my soul is in Cathay.

There's a schooner in the offing,
With her topsails shot with fire,
And my heart has gone aboard her
For the islands of Desire.

I must forth again tomorrow!
With the sunset I must be
Hull down on the trail of rapture
In the wonder of the sea.

—RICHARD HOVEY

DEPARTURE

It's little I care what path I take,
And where it leads it's little I care;
But out of this house, lest my heart break,
I must go, and off somewhere.

It's little I know what's in my heart,
What's in my mind it's little I know,
But there's that in me must up and start,
And it's little I care where my feet go.

I wish I could walk for a day and a night,
And find me at dawn in a desolate place
With never the rut of a road in sight,
Nor the roof of a house, nor the eyes of a face.

I wish I could walk till my blood should spout,
And drop me, never to stir again,
On a shore that is wide, for the tide is out,
And the weedy rocks are bare to the rain.

But dump or dock, where the path I take
Brings up, it's little enough I care;
And it's little I'd mind the fuss they'll make,
Huddled dead in a ditch somewhere.

"Is something the matter, dear?" she said,
"That you sit at your work so silently?"
"No, mother, no, 'twas a knot in my thread.
There goes the kettle, I'll make the tea."

—EDNA ST. VINCENT MILLAY

Wanderlust—the desire to see the unknown—seems to be a characteristic of youth; yet there are disadvantages to being footloose. The lure of foreign lands and the stable comforts of home are often in conflict.

ENVY

I have a brother
    Who has not seen
The white foam flying
    Where tall ships lean;
For he is plowing
    The fields at home,
While I am faring
    The trackless foam.
But while he labors
    Where grass and tree
Are trembling beauty,
    He envies me.

I have a brother
      Whose footsteps turn,
When dusk is falling
      And candles burn,
To where a lassie
      And laddie wait
To hear him open
      The garden gate.
And while I wander
      Far ways and dim,
Though dreams are calling,
      I envy him.

—EDGAR DANIEL KRAMER

Man is a creature of moods, and wanderlust is one of them. Moods, however, can be most strange and unusual. There are times when your mood seems to be intensely real; yet the thoughts that bring it on or that grow out of it are such that you would not dare describe them to your friends—your mood is so personal, so imaginative, perhaps even so "far-fetched" that you would feel strange trying to tell anyone about it.

Many of the following poems speak of inner feelings of this personal nature. The first one has to do with the thoughts that the poet had as she looked at the sky and let her imagination roam.

THE SKY

I saw a shadow on the ground
And heard a bluejay going by;
A shadow went across the ground,
And I looked up and saw the sky.

It hung up on the poplar tree,
But while I looked it did not stay;

It gave a tiny sort of jerk
And moved a little bit away.

And farther on and farther on
It moved and never seemed to stop.
I think it must be tied with chains
And something pulls it from the top.

It never has come down again,
And every time I look to see,
The sky is always slipping back
And getting far away from me.

—ELIZABETH MADOX ROBERTS

Many of you will spend much of your lives working with machines. Certainly almost everyone in the modern world is affected by machines in one way or another. You may already have resented their noise and smell and blind power, just as the next poet did, and you may have looked for something more in tune with human warmth.

MACHINES

I hear them grinding, grinding, through the night,
The gaunt machines with arteries of fire,
Muscled with iron, boweled with smoldering light;
I watch them pulsing, swinging, climbing higher,
Derrick on derrick, wheel on rhythmic wheel,
Swift band on whirring band, lever on lever,
Shouting their songs in raucous notes of steel,
Blinding a village with light, damming a river.
I hear them grinding, grinding, hour on hour,
Cleaving the night in twain, shattering the dark
With all the rasping torrents of their power,
Groaning and belching spark on crimson spark.

I cannot hear my voice above their cry
Shaking the earth and thundering to the sky.

Slowly the dawn comes up. No motors stir
The brightening hilltops as the sunrise flows
In yellow tides where daybreak's lavender
Clings to a waiting valley. No derrick throws
The sun into the heavens and no pulley
Unfolds the wildflowers thirsting for the day;
No wheel unravels ferns deep in a gulley;
No engine starts the brook upon its way.
The butterflies drift idly, wing to wing,
Knowing no measured rhythm they must follow;
No turbine drives the white clouds as they swing
Across the cool blue meadows of the swallow.
With all the feathered silence of a swan
They whir and beat—the engines of the dawn.

—DANIEL WHITEHEAD HICKY

Nature speaks a language that machines never can. Often in your
private thoughts you may find yourself turning away from the things
to which you should be paying attention and letting your mind roam,
leaving the school and the classroom behind, remembering unex-
pectedly a day or a moment that is stored in a corner of your memory.

MEMORY

My mind lets go a thousand things,
Like dates of wars and deaths of kings,
And yet recalls the very hour—
'Twas noon by yonder village tower,
And on the last blue noon in May—
The wind came briskly up this way,
Crisping the brook beside the road;

Then, pausing here, set down its load
Of pine-scents, and shook listlessly
Two petals from that wild-rose tree.

—THOMAS BAILEY ALDRICH

A parent is often at a loss to communicate his feelings to his children and can only reach out silently, hoping to say without words what he feels. Reading this next poem may bring to mind an occasion when one of your parents said something or made a gesture of affection that puzzled you and made you wonder what thoughts lay behind it.

THE FATHER

Hearing his son and daughter
Laugh and talk of dances, theaters,
Of their school, and friends,
And books,
Taking it all for granted—
He sighs a bit,
Remembering wistfully
A certain mill-town
And his boyhood there,
And puts his arm
Across his son's broad shoulder,
Dumbly, as fathers do.

—JOHN HOLMES

The son in "The Father" does not truly know what lies behind his father's gesture; no one can know completely the thoughts and emotions of another person. Sara Teasdale, however, feels that we reveal more of ourselves than we believe we do, even to a passing stranger in the street.

FACES

People that I meet
        In the city's broken roar,
Faces that I lose so soon
        And have never found before.

Do you know how much you tell
        In the meeting of our eyes,
How ashamed I am, and sad
        To have pierced your poor disguise?

Secrets rushing without sound
        Crying from your hiding places—
Let me go, I cannot bear
        The sorrow of the passing faces.

—People in the restless street,
        Can it be, oh can it be
In the meeting of our eyes
        That you know as much of me?

—SARA TEASDALE

Sometimes the gulf that seems to separate people is especially wide, and one discovers too late that it need not have existed at all. Edwin Arlington Robinson reflected on this tragedy in his poem "An Old Story."

AN OLD STORY

Strange that I did not know him then,
        That friend of mine!
I did not even show him then
        One friendly sign;

But cursed him for the ways he had
　　To make me see
My envy of the praise he had
　　For praising me.

I would have rid the earth of him
　　Once, in my pride. . . .
I never knew the worth of him
　　Until he died.

—EDWIN ARLINGTON ROBINSON

The death of a loved one always produces an intensely personal response. The vacancy has to be filled—each person does it in his own way. Edna St. Vincent Millay's "Lament" has a simplicity that makes the unspoken grief following a death intensely real and moving.

LAMENT

Listen, children:
Your father is dead.
From his old coats
I'll make you little jackets;
I'll make you little trousers
From his old pants.
There'll be in his pockets
Things he used to put there,
Keys and pennies
Covered with tobacco;
Dan shall have the pennies
To save in his bank;
Anne shall have the keys
To make a pretty noise with.

Life must go on,
And the dead be forgotten;
Life must go on,
Though good men die;
Anne, eat your breakfast;
Dan, take your medicine;
Life must go on;
I forget just why.

—EDNA ST. VINCENT MILLAY

Robert Louis Stevenson's reflections upon his approaching death serve as his own epitaph, and express his philosophy of life. You will find the mood here quite different from that of "Lament."

REQUIEM

Under the wide and starry sky
    Dig the grave and let me lie:
Glad did I live and gladly die,
    And I laid me down with a will.

This be the verse you 'grave for me:
    Here he lies where he long'd to be;
Home is the sailor, home from sea,
    And the hunter home from the hill.

—ROBERT LOUIS STEVENSON

Moods and memory are very closely connected. If you have experienced a great personal tragedy in your life, perhaps the death of a relative or close friend, you know how the small, everyday business of life and home will cause you to reflect upon your loss.

SOLITUDE

When you have tidied all things for the night,
And while your thoughts are fading to their sleep,
You'll pause a moment in the late firelight,
Too sorrowful to weep.

The large and gentle furniture has stood
In sympathetic silence all the day
With that old kindness of domestic wood;
Nevertheless the haunted room will say:
"Some one must be away."

The little dog rolls over half awake,
Stretches his paws, yawns, looking up at you,
Wags his tail very slightly for your sake,
That you may feel he is unhappy too.

A distant engine whistles, or the floor
Creaks, or the wandering night-wind bangs a door.

Silence is scattered like a broken glass.
The minutes prick their ears and run about,
Then one by one subside again and pass
Sedately in, monotonously out.

You bend your head and wipe away a tear.
Solitude walks one heavy step more near.

—HAROLD MONRO

In the next poem Sara Teasdale is looking back into the past and
thinking about something that happened years ago. As you read her
words, think about these questions: Has she accepted her loss? When
she says "Let it be forgotten," will she really forget? Is the pain gone,
if not the memory?

"LET IT BE FORGOTTEN"

> Let it be forgotten, as a flower is forgotten,
>   Forgotten as a fire that once was singing gold,
> Let it be forgotten for ever and ever,
>   Time is a kind friend, he will make us old.
>
> If anyone asks, say it was forgotten
>   Long and long ago,
> As a flower, as a fire, as a hushed footfall
>   In a long forgotten snow.
>   —SARA TEASDALE

Sara Teasdale wrote many poems about the personal reaction to the loss of loved ones through death or separation. In "Wisdom" she concludes with a profound statement that has great truth in it, as you will see when you have grasped it fully.

WISDOM

> It was a night of early spring,
>   The winter-sleep was scarcely broken;
> Around us shadows and the wind
>   Listened for what was never spoken.
>
> Though half a score of years are gone,
>   Spring comes as sharply now as then—
> But if we had it all to do
>   It would be done the same again.
>
> It was a spring that never came,
>   But we have lived enough to know
> What we have never had, remains;
>   It is the things we have that go.
>   —SARA TEASDALE

In the introduction to this chapter, it was stated that the poets have written of many different moods, not just the dark ones about which you have been reading in the last few poems. Perhaps the most famous statement of personal well-being in the English language is this next small "song" by Robert Browning.

SONG FROM "PIPPA PASSES"

> The year's at the spring
> The day's at the morn;
> Morning's at seven;
> The hillside's dew-pearled;
> The lark's on the wing;
> The snail's on the thorn:
> God's in his heaven—
> All's right with the world!
>
> —ROBERT BROWNING

The next poem is scarcely more than a passing thought, written down by the poet almost exactly as it occurred to him. You have probably had many such ideas without realizing that they are the material from which poems are made. Remember this little verse when you begin to write poetry yourself.

THE RED WHEELBARROW

> so much depends
> upon
>
> a red wheel
> barrow
>
> glazed with rain
> water
>
> beside the white
> chickens
>
> —WILLIAM CARLOS WILLIAMS

Your thoughtful reflections may spring from almost any source. "The Red Wheelbarrow" was a single thought based on the simplest observation. Andrew Lang, in a more elaborate poem, watches mowers using their scythes, and he reflects upon the soft sounds and rhythmic movements that are lulling him into a mood of great tranquility.

SCYTHE SONG

Mowers, weary and brown, and blithe,
    What is the word methinks ye know,
Endless over-word that the Scythe
    Sings to the blades of the grass below?
Scythes that swing in the grass and clover,
    Something, still, they say as they pass;
What is the word that, over and over,
    Sings the Scythe to the flowers and grass?

Hush, ah, hush, the Scythes are saying,
    Hush, and heed not, and fall asleep;
Hush, they say to the grasses swaying,
    Hush, they sing to the clover deep!
Hush—'tis the lullaby Time is singing—
    Hush, and heed not, for all things pass,
Hush, ah, hush! and the Scythes are swinging
    Over the clover, over the grass!

—ANDREW LANG

In the last several pages you have been reading poems reflecting many moods—loneliness, solitude, wanderlust, well-being. How often, when you have been lost in your own thoughts, have you come back to reality suddenly, thankful that you are once again in the familiar world that you know so well? The final poem in this chapter may remind you of just such an occasion, when you put aside your reflections and happily took up again the business of everyday living.

THE SHELL

And then I pressed the shell
Close to my ear
And listened well,
And straightway like a bell
Came low and clear
The slow, sad murmur of the distant seas,
Whipped by an icy breeze
Upon a shore
Wind-swept and desolate.
It was a sunless strand that never bore
The footprint of a man,
Nor felt the weight
Since time began
Of any human quality or stir
Save what the dreary winds and waves incur.
And in the hush of waters was the sound
Of pebbles rolling round,
For ever rolling with a hollow sound.
And bubbling sea-weeds as the waters go
Swish to and fro
Their long, cold tentacles of slimy gray.
There was no day,
Nor ever came a night
Setting the stars alight
To wonder at the moon:
Was twilight only and the frightened croon,
Smitten to whimpers, of the dreary wind
And waves that journeyed blind—
And then I loosed my ear . . . O, it was sweet
To hear a cart go jolting down the street.

—JAMES STEPHENS

1. In Robert Frost's poem "The Armful" what do you think the "armful" represents? Write a paragraph or two describing a day in your life that made you feel like the person in this poem.

2. "The World Is Too Much with Us" criticizes our society today just as much as that of the poet's day. What are the main points he is making?

3. If you were engaged in a debate with William Wordsworth, he defending his viewpoint and you defending yours, how would you criticize his ideas?

4. How might the dog in Harold Monro's poem symbolize a way of life much desired by many people in today's busy world?

5. What would you say is the message of "Cobbler" for all people and all professions?

6. "Caliban in the Coal Mines" may be interpreted completely without ever mentioning coal mines or miners. Thinking of the poem in this symbolic way, explain its deeper meaning.

7. What is Paul Engle saying in "Cat's Eye" about the importance to him of man in the universe? In what way is the "magnificence of a human face" so different from the things the poet describes in the earlier lines?

8. "Travel" speaks of "embers red on the sky," a sight which is seldom seen in our age of diesel locomotives. Does the out-of-date reference weaken the meaning of the poem? Explain why you feel as you do.

9. "Sea Gypsy" has the same basic theme as "Travel." Of the two poems, which do you consider the better? Explain how you made your choice, paying attention to such poetic devices as similes, metaphors, and other techniques that you feel make a difference between the two.

10. Day-dreaming is an activity with which you are familiar. In "Departure" how does the poet tell you that the poem is mainly concerned with day-dreams?

11. Edna St. Vincent Millay does not say exactly where she would like to go—she speaks only of the desire to see new places and have new experiences. If you could travel wherever you wished, where would it be? Why do you want to go there?

12. Of the two lives described in Edgar Daniel Kramer's poem, which would you choose? Why?

13. "The Sky" is a very personal observation, so imaginative that it seems almost humorous in places. Why do you think the average person would hesitate to tell other people of his thoughts that might be like the ones in this poem?

14. The poet of "Machines" is telling you to keep your vision clear so that you can see the real values of life. What does he feel these values are?

15. There are certain similarities in the viewpoints expressed in "Machines" and "Cat's Eye," although the poems are in many ways different. What similarities can you find?

16. Thomas Bailey Aldrich describes memory as being unpredictable. Why is it that you remember some things that are not "important" and forget others that are supposed to be significant?

17. In John Holmes's poem, what do you think the father is trying to say through his gesture?

18. Is the situation as described in "The Father" a very common experience between parents and their children? What are the differences between parent and child that seem to make communication difficult?

19. Why was Sara Teasdale "ashamed" to have "pierced" the "poor disguise" of the people she observed in "Faces"?

20. What does "Faces" tell you about yourself and other people? What is Sara Teasdale's point in the final stanza?

21. Why is the title of the poem "An Old Story" particularly appropriate to the subject of the poem?

22. The second stanza of "An Old Story" tells why the speaker hated the man who died. What was the reason for this hatred?

23. In Edna St. Vincent Millay's "Lament," what pair of lines do you find give you the greatest sense of tragedy? Explain your choice.

24. Robert Louis Stevenson's poem "Requiem" is very descriptive of his own life. What do you think are some of the qualities that made him such a great man?

25. Stevenson was neither a sailor nor a hunter. Why did he use these terms to describe himself?

26. "Solitude" uses the old poetic technique of *personification* to great advantage. List at least five uses of this device within the poem.

27. The stanzas in "Solitude" are not all of the same length. Why do you think the poet chose to vary them as he did?

28. In "Let It Be Forgotten" the poet speaks of time as a "kind old friend." In what way has time proved friendly to the author? How does this idea fit into the over-all meaning of the poem?

29. In "Wisdom" what do you think it was that was "never spoken"?

30. The last two lines of "Wisdom" seem very simple, at least on the surface. Explain what you think the poet means by the things that "go" and those that "remain."

31. Why did Robert Browning, in the "Song from *Pippa Passes*," put in the same sentence two such unlike creatures as the soaring lark and the lowly snail?

32. "The Red Wheelbarrow," which is really an image rather than a poem, suggests many things with its line "so much depends." What do you think the poet is trying to say to you by "depends," as he uses it here?

33. "Scythe Song" has within its lines several examples of a very interesting poetic technique. You may have noticed that the word "hush" sounds like the actual sound made as a scythe cuts through the long grass. This use of a word which sounds like what is being described has the long name of *onomatopoeia*. You frequently use onomatopoeia —think of such words as crash, bang, puff, howl. Find at least three examples of onomatopoeia among the other poems in this chapter. "Cat's Eye" would be a good place to start looking.

34. "The Shell" has a rather surprising ending: the poet was very glad to hear the "cart go jolting down the street." What feelings had the sounds of the shell produced that made him glad to hear the old familiar cart?

CHAPTER NINE

Nature

Every year more and more people leave the countryside to live in the growing cities of America. If you happen to be a city-dweller, your contacts with nature may seem somewhat limited. Nature, however, has a way of following you wherever you may go. Even in the big cities there are parks and gardens; the winds blow and the rains come down as the seasons change; the trees put forth their leaves in the spring and shed them in the fall; and in these days of easy travel, the country isn't very far away, after all. Sunday picnics, trips to the seashore, vacations in the mountains, a pot of geraniums on the window sill, a little dog or a cat or a canary as part of the family—these show how almost everyone feels a kinship with nature and tries to keep in touch with it, no matter where he may live.

The number of poems written about nature is probably greater than that of all other types of poems combined. The poet, as you must now realize, speaks of the things that are meaningful to almost everyone; so it is not at all strange that he writes frequently about the beauty of the out-of-doors and of man's relationship to his surroundings. Most poets feel that man is a part of nature, even though he may at times forget that he is, and many poems are written to remind the reader not to forget his link with his natural environment.

Nature-poetry comes in many sizes and shapes, and speaks with many voices. The poems in this chapter are divided into three main types: (1) poetry based upon the seasons of the year, (2) poetry having to do with animals and wild life, and (3) poetry that looks at nature in a more general way, random glimpses of the natural world. Some of it whispers; some of it almost shouts. Of the many poems included in the following selections, there should be more than a few that will speak directly to you.

THE SEASONS

The wonderful variety of the seasons has been the subject of many poems. When you first look out of the window in the morning, you may feel an emotional response that a poet has also experienced and put into words. Especially in the spring, your thoughts are likely to be happy and forward-looking. Can you sense the feeling a thawing wind gave to poet Robert Frost?

TO THE THAWING WIND

Come with rain, O loud Southwester!
Bring the singer, bring the nester;
Give the buried flower a dream;
Make the settled snow-bank steam;
Find the brown beneath the white;
But whate'er you do tonight,
Bathe my window, make it flow,
Melt it as the ice will go;
Melt the glass and leave the sticks
Like a hermit's crucifix;
Burst into my narrow stall;
Swing the picture on the wall;
Run the rattling pages o'er;
Scatter poems on the floor;
Turn the poet out of door.

—ROBERT FROST

Spring is the time of the year when you feel that life is promising many things to you, that the days and months ahead hold countless happy moments. For young children, spring may be the best season of the year; nobody enjoys it in quite the way they do. E. E. Cummings captures their feelings perfectly in these lines:

CHANSON INNOCENTE

in Just-
spring   when the world is mud-
luscious the little
lame balloonman

whistles   far   and wee
and eddicandbill come
running from marbles and
piracies and it's
spring

when the world is puddle-wonderful

the queer
old balloonman whistles
far   and   wee
and bettyandisbel come dancing

from hop-scotch and jump-rope and
it's
spring
and

        the
              goat-footed
balloonMan   whistles
far
and
wee   —E. E. CUMMINGS

As the months pass and spring gives way to early summer, new experiences appear on the horizon. The next poem suggests the promise of the days that lie ahead.

By these signs
    You shall know
Where to find me,
    When to go.

When the lilacs'
    Fitful shade
By the open door
    Is laid,

You will hear the brook's
    Thin tunes,
Through the fragrant
    Afternoons.

Listen for me
    When it sings
Through the jeweled
    Evenings.

Come on tiptoe
    And surprise
Bullfrogs catching
    Fireflies.

Over faggot,
    Over fern,
By the deepest
    Trout-pool, turn.

Lift one hand
    And to your lip,
Lightly touch
    Your finger tip.

From the dusky
 Forest floor,
A fleeting step,
 An opened door.

May has left
 A breathless hour;
Gone the leaf,
 But comes the flower.

Silence dies—
 The stars appear,
The world leaps forward,
 June is here!

      —JOAN ELISABETH ROSÉ

The warm days of summer inspire many thoughts. Robert Louis Stevenson, a favorite poet of many young people, thinks of the sun as a gardener who brings beauty to the world by his warmth and care.

SUMMER SUN

Great is the sun, and wide he goes
Through empty heaven without repose;
And in the blue and glowing days
More thick than rain he showers his rays.

Though closer still the blinds we pull
To keep the shady parlour cool,
Yet he will find a chink or two
To slip his golden fingers through.

The dusty attic, spider-clad,
He, through the keyhole, maketh glad;

And through the broken edge of tiles
Into the laddered hay-loft smiles.

Meantime his golden face around
He bares to all the garden ground,
And sheds a warm and glittering look
Among the ivy's inmost nook.

Above the hills, along the blue,
Round the bright air with footing true,
To please the child, to paint the rose,
The gardener of the World, he goes.

—ROBERT LOUIS STEVENSON

The long, lazy summer seems endless: school is far away, weeks
and weeks stretch out ahead, and time seems almost to stand still.
James Hogg, writing a century and a half ago, speaks of summer's
leisurely freedom in language that is appropriate even today.

A BOY'S SONG

Where the pools are bright and deep,
Where the gray trout lies asleep,
Up the river and o'er the lea,
That's the way for Billy and me.

Where the blackbird sings the latest,
Where the hawthorn blooms the sweetest,
Where the nestlings chirp and flee,
That's the way for Billy and me.

Where the mowers mow the cleanest,
Where the hay lies thick and greenest;
There to trace the homeward bee,
That's the way for Billy and me.

Where the hazel bank is steepest,
Where the shadow falls the deepest,
Where the clustering nuts fall free,
That's the way for Billy and me.

Why the boys should drive away
Little maidens from their play,
Or love to banter and fight so well,
That's the thing I never could tell.

But this I know, I love to play,
Through the meadow, among the hay;
Up the water and o'er the lea,
That's the way for Billy and me.

—JAMES HOGG

The summer pleasures for "Billy and me" are not permanent ones, however. Sooner than seems possible, autumn is here again, and with it come the harvesting and preparing for winter.

NOVEMBER

When the ground squirrel toils at gathering wheat,
And the wood dove's somber notes repeat
The story of autumn's passing feet;

When the cold, gray sky has a rushing breeze
Which hums in the grass like a hive of bees,
And scatters the leaves from the roaring trees;

When the corn is filled with a rising moan,
And the gray crane flies on his course alone,
Hastening south to the orange zone—

Then the boy on the bare, brown prairie knows
That winter is coming with drifting snows
To cover the grave of the dry, dead rose.

—HAMLIN GARLAND

Finally comes the snow; the old year is nearly gone. The special beauty of summer and autumn is replaced by winter's own charms. Robert Frost, pausing in the winter woods at night, felt a quiet response to the tranquil evening—a response that is deeper than the words might seem.

STOPPING BY WOODS
ON A SNOWY EVENING

Whose woods these are I think I know.
His house is in the village though;
He will not see me stopping here
To watch his woods fill up with snow.

My little horse must think it queer
To stop without a farmhouse near
Between the woods and frozen lake
The darkest evening of the year.

He gives his harness bells a shake
To ask if there is some mistake.
The only other sound's the sweep
Of easy wind and downy flake.

The woods are lovely, dark and deep.
But I have promises to keep,
And miles to go before I sleep,
And miles to go before I sleep.

—ROBERT FROST

ANIMALS AND WILD LIFE

Not many years ago it was still possible to see wild horses in some parts of our country. These animals—tough, intelligent, beautiful creatures—are now rare, and it is a lucky person who manages to catch sight of one. In the poem that follows, the writer describes his reactions upon seeing these wild, exciting animals.

WILD MARES RUNNING

Under the breast of a crimson hill
By a desert pool, at close of day—
I saw three horses, three wild mares
Running, at play.

Three wild mares, their light feet stamping—
Arching their shining necks; their eyes glowing;
Running across the crimson light,
The dark manes flowing.

Aye . . . to recapture that lovely hour,
Fled with the feet of the wild mares going,
Under the veils of the winter dusk,
Beyond all knowing!

—FRANK SWAIN

The sight of a wild deer in its natural surroundings is always thrilling. However, in Edna St. Vincent Millay's poem "The Buck in the Snow," the picture is tinged with tragedy.

THE BUCK IN THE SNOW

White sky, over the hemlocks bowed with snow,
Saw you not at the beginning of evening the antlered buck and his
    doe
Standing in the apple-orchard? I saw them. I saw them suddenly
    go,
Tails up, with long leaps lovely and slow,
Over the stone-wall into the wood of hemlocks bowed with snow.

Now lies he here, his wild blood scalding the snow.

How strange a thing is death, bringing to his knees, bringing to his
    antlers
The buck in the snow.

How strange a thing,—a mile away by now, it may be,
Under the heavy hemlocks that as the moments pass
Shift their loads a little, letting fall a feather of snow—
Life, looking out attentive from the eyes of the doe.

—EDNA ST. VINCENT MILLAY

Lew Sarett also wrote of a tragic event in nature. Man and the animals of the forest are often at odds, and the following poem speaks of this unequal struggle.

FOUR LITTLE FOXES

Speak gently, Spring, and make no sudden sound;
For in my windy valley, yesterday I found
New-born foxes squirming on the ground—
      Speak gently.

Walk softly, March, forbear the bitter blow;
Her feet within a trap, her blood upon the snow,
The four little foxes saw their mother go—
      Walk softly.

Go lightly, Spring, Oh give them no alarm;
When I covered them with boughs to shelter them from harm,
The thin blue foxes suckled at my arm—
      Go lightly.

Step softly, March, with your rampant hurricane;
Nuzzling one another, and whimpering with pain,
The new little foxes are shivering in the rain—
      Step softly.

—LEW SARETT

It is often amazing to the city-bred person to see how perfectly nature has provided for the creatures that must live under the harsh

laws of the wild. In the two poems that follow, the writers express
their wonder at the marvelous instincts and perfection of form that
enable the animals to survive.

SOMETHING TOLD THE WILD GEESE

> Something told the wild geese
>   It was time to go.
> Though the fields lay golden
>   Something whispered, "Snow."
>
> Leaves were green and stirring,
>   Berries, luster-glossed,
> But beneath warm feathers
>   Something cautioned, "Frost."
>
> All the sagging orchards
>   Steamed with amber spice,
> But each wild breast stiffened
>   At remembered ice.
>
> Something told the wild geese
>   It was time to fly,—
> Summer sun was on their wings,
>   Winter in their cry.   —RACHEL FIELD

THE EAGLE

> He clasps the crag with crooked hands;
> Close to the sun in lonely lands
> Ringed with the azure world, he stands.
>
> The wrinkled sea beneath him crawls;
> He watches from his mountain walls,
> And like a thunderbolt he falls.
>
>   —ALFRED, LORD TENNYSON

There are several animals that exist both in a wild state and as the domesticated companions of man. The wild horses that you read about have had relatives that have served man's needs and pleasure for centuries. You may not have realized that there are wild dogs, too, as well as the gentle pets that you love. Here are two poems about dogs, showing two very different animals.

LONE DOG

I'm a lean dog, a keen dog, a wild dog, and lone;
I'm a rough dog, a tough dog, hunting on my own;
I'm a bad dog, a mad dog, teasing silly sheep;
I love to sit and bay the moon, to keep fat souls from sleep.

I'll never be a lap dog, licking dirty feet,
A sleek dog, a meek dog, cringing for my meat,
Not for me the fireside, the well-filled plate,
But shut door, and sharp stone, and cuff and kick, and hate.

Not for me the other dogs running by my side,
Some have run a short while, but none of them would bide.
O, mine is still the lone trail, the hard trail, the best,
Wide wind, and wild stars, and hunger of the quest!

—IRENE R. MCLEOD

LITTLE DOGS

Some little dogs are shaggy,
    Some little dogs are shaved;
Most little dogs are waggy
    And properly behaved.

Some little dogs wear blankets,
Some little dogs wear boots;
Most little dogs go naked,
    But some have union suits.

205   *NATURE*

Some little dogs are Betty,
Some little dogs are Bill;
But all little dogs may call on me
When and where they will!

—ARTHUR GUITERMAN

The most common tame animal is the cat. It is truly a self-sufficient creature, able to accustom itself to almost any situation. The
cat described in the next poem may remind you of one you know.

MILK FOR THE CAT

When the tea is brought at five o'clock
And all the neat curtains are drawn with care,
The little black cat with bright green eyes
Is suddenly purring there.

At first she pretends, having nothing to do,
She has come in merely to blink by the grate,
But, though tea may be late or the milk may be sour,
She is never late.

And presently her agate eyes
Take a soft large milky haze,
And her independent casual glance
Becomes a stiff hard gaze.

Then she stamps her claws or lifts her ears
Or twists her tail and begins to stir,
Till suddenly all her lithe body becomes
One breathing trembling purr.

The children eat and wriggle and laugh;
The two old ladies stroke their silk:
But the cat is grown small and thin with desire,
Transformed to a creeping lust for milk.

The white saucer like some full moon descends
At last from the clouds of the table above;
She sighs and dreams and thrills and glows,
Transfigured with love.

She nestles over the shining rim,
Buries her chin in the creamy sea;
Her tail hangs loose; each drowsy paw
Is doubled under each bending knee.

A long dim ecstasy holds her life;
Her world is an infinite shapeless white,
Till her tongue has curled the last holy drop,
Then she sinks back into the night,

Draws and dips her body to heap
Her sleepy nerves in the great arm-chair,
Lies defeated and buried deep
Three or four hours unconscious there.

—HAROLD MONRO

RANDOM GLIMPSES

No matter where you live, there is much to see and enjoy in nature. Just as important as the enjoyment you derive from it, however, is the beneficial effect nature has on you, often restoring your sense of balance in a topsy-turvy world.

The first two poems in this section, "The Little Cares" and "Green Escape," both reflect calming influences that nature can so often provide.

THE LITTLE CARES

The little cares that fretted me,
I lost them yesterday,
Among the fields above the sea,
Among the winds at play;

Among the lowing of the herds,
The rustling of the trees,
Among the singing of the birds,
The humming of the bees.
The foolish fears of what may happen,
I cast them all away,
Among the clover-scented grass,
Among the new-mown hay,
Among the husking of the corn
Where drowsy poppies nod,
Where ill thoughts die, and good are born,
Out in the fields with God.

—ELIZABETH BARRETT BROWNING

GREEN ESCAPE

I have turned my face
Away from streets and crowds
To a windy place
And clouds.

I have turned from skyscrapers
That scratch out the sky,
From wet newspapers
Always whipping by.

I have taken away my heart,
I will give it again
To be split apart
By wind and rain.

I will stand like a stone
All day in the grass
Where the bees drone
And pass and repass.

I will watch them brush
Gold across their legs,
Hear the bird at hush
Over her eggs.

I will hear the wild swan
Lift high and harsh
His crooked clarion
Across the marsh.

Where the jewel-weed hangs,
Where the spotted stream runs,
Where the green beetle bangs
Bronze on bronze—

Rooted in the deep ground,
The sky tugging at my hair,
There will I be found—
There!

—JOSEPH AUSLANDER

Always a subject that has stirred the imagination of man, the sea has been a strong inspiration to countless poets. Probably the most famous of the sea-poets is John Masefield, whose "Sea-Fever" is one of the best-known poems in the English language.

SEA-FEVER

I must down to the seas again, to the lonely sea and the sky,
And all I ask is a tall ship and a star to steer her by;
And the wheel's kick and the wind's song and the white sail's shaking,
And a gray mist on the sea's face and a gray dawn breaking.

I must down to the seas again, for the call of the running tide
Is a wild call and a clear call that may not be denied;
And all I ask is a windy day with the white clouds flying,
And the flung spray and the blown spume, and the sea-gulls crying.

I must down to the seas again, to the vagrant gypsy life.
To the gull's way and the whale's way where the wind's like a whet-
    ted knife;
And all I ask is a merry yarn from a laughing fellow-rover,
And quiet sleep and a sweet dream when the long trick's over.

                        —JOHN MASEFIELD

Dawn along the seacoast has a special quality. If you have ever experienced this remarkable moment, Isabel Butchart's poem may remind you of the feelings you had at daybreak by the shore.

D A W N

    A drifting mist beyond the bar,
      A light that is no light,
    A line of gray where breakers are,
      And in the distance—night.

    The watching lamps along the coasts
      Shine wanly on the foam,
    And silently, like tired ghosts,
      The fishing fleet comes home.

                        —ISABEL BUTCHART

Robert Frost spoke often of nature, and the simplicity of many of his poems shows a deep understanding that goes far beyond his words. Could you resist the invitation he extends in "The Pasture"?

THE PASTURE

I'm going out to clean the pasture spring;
I'll only stop to rake the leaves away
(And wait to watch the water clear, I may):
I sha'n't be gone long.—You come too.

I'm going out to fetch the little calf
That's standing by the mother. It's so young,
It totters when she licks it with her tongue.
I sha'n't be gone long. —You come too.

—ROBERT FROST

Sometimes the beauties of nature fill you with wonder. A sudden thunderstorm, an unexpected view of the countryside, a spectacular sunset—such things as these can produce a deep response. In the following poem the writer, surveying a beautiful English scene, puts a profound feeling of wonder into words.

THE SPLENDOR FALLS ON CASTLE WALLS

The splendor falls on castle walls
    And snowy summits old in story;
The long light shakes across the lakes,
    And the wild cataract leaps in glory.
Blow, bugle, blow, set the wild echoes flying,
Blow, bugle; answer, echoes, dying, dying, dying.

Oh, hark, Oh, hear! how thin and clear,
    And thinner, clearer, farther going!
Oh, sweet and far from cliff and scar
    The horns of Elfland faintly blowing!
Blow, let us hear the purple glens replying,
Blow, bugle; answer, echoes, dying, dying, dying.

Oh, love, they die in yon rich sky,
They faint on hill or field or river;
Our echoes roll from soul to soul,
And grow forever and forever.
Blow, bugle, blow, set the wild echoes flying,
And answer, echoes, answer, dying, dying, dying.

—ALFRED, LORD TENNYSON

North of Tennyson's England are the famous hills of Scotland. They take on a particular beauty to anyone for whom they have been home, and who must leave them to journey elsewhere. The great Scottish poet Robert Burns wrote of his beloved "Highlands" in this well-known poem.

MY HEART'S IN THE HIGHLANDS

My heart's in the Highlands, my heart is not here;
My heart's in the Highlands a-chasing the deer;
Chasing the wild deer, and following the roe,
My heart's in the Highlands wherever I go.
Farewell to the Highlands, farewell to the North,
The birth place of valor, the country of worth!
Wherever I wander, wherever I rove,
The hills of the Highlands forever I love.

Farewell to the mountains, high-covered with snow!
Farewell to the straths and green valleys below!
Farewell to the forests and wild hanging woods!
Farewell to the torrents and loud-pouring floods!
My heart's in the Highlands, my heart is not here;
My heart's in the Highlands, a-chasing the deer;
Chasing the wild deer, and following the roe,
My heart's in the Highlands wherever I go.

—ROBERT BURNS

You need not travel to Scotland or England to feel the effect of the highlands. Anyone who has been in the hills and mountains of our own country can sense their eternal quality, as did Marion Doyle.

ONLY MOUNTAINS

I know so little of the sky,
That opened book upon whose pages
Is written in stars the history
Of future and the bygone ages.
I know so little: like the brook,
The restless waterfall and river,
I have no time to stop and look,
Like them, I hurry, hurry ever—
Hurry to reach the sea and then
Hurry back to the hills again.
Scurry and scramble—that is why
We know so little of the sky,
The winds, the waters, you and I.
Trees have learned a thing or two
Of those golden words on blue,
But only mountains, still, apart,
Know the manuscript by heart.

—MARION DOYLE

Nature seems "pure" to the poet. He and many other people are often deeply distressed when the hand of man disturbs this purity. A freeway gouging through a forest, a gaudy billboard blocking a sea view, a pile of beer cans defacing a park—sights such as these usually trouble the poet. Sometimes, however, he will see things in a different light; he sees progress as necessary to mankind, and progress is not always accompanied by beauty. Chicago, now a great, noisy city, was once a small town, bordered on three sides by open prairie and on the north by a majestic lake. Today, the picture is very different.

CHICAGO

Hog Butcher for the World,
Tool Maker, Stacker of Wheat,
Player with Railroads and the Nation's Freight Handler;
Stormy, husky, brawling,
City of the Big Shoulders:

They tell me you are wicked and I believe them, for I have seen your
painted women under the gas lamps luring the farm boys.

And they tell me you are crooked and I answer: Yes, it is true I have
seen the gunman kill and go free to kill again.

And they tell me you are brutal and my reply is: On the faces of
women and children I have seen the marks of wanton hunger.

And having answered so I turn once more to those who sneer at this
my city and I give them back the sneer and say to them:

Come and show me another city with lifted head singing so proud to
be alive and coarse and strong and cunning.

Flinging magnetic curses amid the toil of piling job on job, here is a
tall bold slugger set vivid against the little soft cities;

Fierce as a dog with tongue lapping for action, cunning as a savage
pitted against the wilderness,

Bareheaded,
Shoveling,
Wrecking,
Planning,
Building, breaking, rebuilding,

Under the smoke, dust all over his mouth, laughing with white
teeth,

Under the terrible burden of destiny laughing as a young man laughs,

Laughing even as an ignorant fighter laughs who has never lost a
battle,

Bragging and laughing that under his wrist is the pulse, and under
his ribs the heart of the people,

Laughing!

Laughing the stormy, husky, brawling laughter of Youth, half-naked, sweating, proud to be Hog Butcher, Tool Maker, Stacker of Wheat, Player with Railroads and Freight Handler to the Nation.

—CARL SANDBURG

Another poet, George Bond, sees the Chicago of Carl Sandburg's poem as a temporary blemish on nature's purity. As you read his lines, picture yourself in the open vastness of the unspoiled prairie.

A SUMMER NIGHT

Only the locusts cry in the black midnight,
Only the wind stirs in the lonely grass.
No light, no other life, no other sound—
Only the vast, black prairie and the dim, limitless space where the worlds revolve.
And in the dark the prairie lies awake and restless,
Impatient of man's control, hating his cities and his fences and himself,
Waiting for him to join the mammoth and the laelaps,
Knowing his time will come, and waiting, waiting, waiting,
Biding her time to rise and cover him up;
Dreaming a dream of cities, silent, deserted,
And of prairie grass creeping slowly over their ruins;
Dreaming a dream of a tyrant overcome, and of many, many bones beneath the thick, wild flowers;
Dreaming a dream of many years of silence, broken only by the song of the wind and the cry of the locust.

—GEORGE BOND

Whether you live in a teeming city or on a disappearing prairie or on an unchanging mountain, you cannot view the stars without feeling a deep sense of humility. Sara Teasdale responded to the awe-inspiring beauty of the stars in this way:

STARS

> Alone in the night
>   On a dark hill
> With pines around me
>   Spicy and still,
>
> And a heaven full of stars
>   Over my head,
> White and topaz
>   And misty red;
>
> Myriads with beating
>   Hearts of fire
> That aeons
>   Cannot vex or tire;
>
> Up the dome of heaven
>   Like a great hill,
> I watch them marching
>   Stately and still,
>
> And I know that I
>   Am honored to be
> Witness
>   Of so much majesty.

—SARA TEASDALE

It is interesting to see how two poets react differently to a particular glimpse of nature. The two poems that follow show such a variation clearly. The moon has intrigued poets for thousands of years; here are two views of it.

SILVER

Slowly, silently, now the moon
Walks the night in her silver shoon;
This way, and that, she peers, and sees
Silver fruit upon silver trees;
One by one the casements catch
Her beams beneath the silvery thatch;
Couched in his kennel, like a log,
With paws of silver sleeps the dog;
From their shadowy cote the white breasts peep
Of doves in a silver-feathered sleep;
A harvest mouse goes scampering by,
With silver claws and a silver eye;
And moveless fish in the water gleam,
By silver reeds in a silver stream.

—WALTER DE LA MARE

THE WANING MOON

And like a dying lady, lean and pale,
Who totters forth, wrapt in a gauzy veil,
Out of her chamber, led by the insane
And feeble wanderings of her fading brain,
The moon arose up in the murky East,
A white and shapeless mass.

—PERCY BYSSHE SHELLEY

You may remember that the wind in "The Highwayman" was "a torrent of darkness," and in one of Robert Frost's poems it was the fresh, snow-thawing breath of spring. The final two poems in this chapter show, once again, how poets respond differently to the same subject.

WHO HAS SEEN THE WIND?

Who has seen the wind?
  Neither I nor you:
But when the leaves hang trembling
  The wind is passing thro'.

Who has seen the wind?
  Neither you nor I:
But when the trees bow down their heads
  The wind is passing by.

—CHRISTINA GEORGINA ROSSETTI

DO YOU FEAR THE FORCE OF THE WIND?

Do you fear the force of the wind,
The slash of the rain?
Go face them and fight them,
Be savage again.

Go hungry and cold like the wolf,
    Go wade like the crane:
The palms of your hands will thicken,
The skin of your cheek will tan,
You'll grow ragged and weary and swarthy,
    But you'll walk like a man!

—HAMLIN GARLAND

LOOKING BEYOND THE WORDS

The Seasons

1. In everyday language, what are the various signs of winter's end that Robert Frost wishes for in his poem "To the Thawing Wind"?

2. The poem "To the Thawing Wind" is almost like a song that slowly builds itself toward a final burst of melody; in other words, there is a kind of ending that *must come* because of what the poet has told you.

Explain why the ending—"Turn the poet out of door"—is so right for this poem.

3. How does the unusual arrangement of the various lines and words of the poem "Chanson Innocente" emphasize certain ideas that the poet was trying to communicate?

4. What similarities and differences do you notice in the method of line structure in the poems "I Come" and "Chanson Innocente"?

5. "Summer Sun" uses personification to emphasize its message. Write two sentences in which you use this technique, one personifying the word "school," and the other the word "moon."

6. "A Boy's Song" was written more than a hundred and fifty years ago; yet in many ways it speaks of pleasures that can be enjoyed today. What is there about the poem that makes it so timeless?

7. The poem "November" has an unusual rhyme scheme. To guard against becoming repetitious, however, the poet has also used a system of light and heavy sounds within the poem itself. Copy the first stanza and be prepared to point out which syllables are sharp, heavy sounds and which are light, soft sounds.

8. In "Stopping by Woods on a Snowy Evening," there is, first of all, a fine description of a sleigh ride through a snow-covered landscape. Many readers feel, however, that there is a deeper, more serious side to this poem, quite apart from the obvious picture. Try to interpret this second level of meaning.

Wild Life

9. Frank Swain, in "Wild Mares Running," does two things: (1) he describes the beautiful animals, and (2) he reflects upon the scene as he remembers it. What is his response to this recollected experience?

10. Lew Sarett's "Four Little Foxes" and Edna St. Vincent Millay's "The Buck in the Snow" both place man in a cruel light; yet the poems say nothing directly about man. Do you think the poems would have been better if the events had been more clearly described? What would have been the result?

11. In the two poems about birds, "Something Told the Wild Geese" and "The Eagle," the poets make you wonder about the very meaning of life itself. Explain how they accomplish this goal.

12. "Long Dog" and "Little Dogs" are very different in content. Which type of dog did you personally find more to your liking as you read the poems? Explain the reasons for your choice.

13. The descriptive language used in the poem "Milk for the Cat" seems to give an accurate picture of the cat and its actions. Give some examples of the words and phrases that paint this picture so well.

Random Glimpses

14. Elizabeth Barrett Browning seems to feel that the beauties of nature have a definite effect on man. Do you think that response to nature is a common experience? Can you give an illustration from your own knowledge which shows that the poet is correct or incorrect in her views?

15. Joseph Auslander, in the poem "Green Escape," seems to feel the same way as Mrs. Browning about the good effects of nature. What added thoughts does he express?

16. You can see a certain charm in John Masefield's poem "Sea Fever" that might help explain why sailors can spend years on the sea and never tire of it. What are some of the qualities of the sea that are so alluring?

17. Most of the poem "Dawn" is simply fine description. What effect is gained by the use of terms like "tired ghosts" and "watching lamps"?

18. What special qualities of Robert Frost's did you learn about as you read the poem "The Pasture"?

19. In "The Splendor Falls," by Alfred, Lord Tennyson, the writer uses the term "Elfland." Why did he choose this word? Why, too, does he use so much repetition in the last lines of each stanza?

20. Robert Burns's poem "My Heart's in the Highlands" uses many words and phrases several times; you have probably often been told to avoid

repetition in your own prose writing, but you would certainly agree that the repetition in this poem provides an added quality. What does it accomplish?

21. Why is it that the poet of "Only Mountains" feels that the mountains "Know the manuscript by heart"? What is it about the poet—or about you, for that matter—that prevents him from knowing the "manuscript" of life?

22. In "Chicago" Carl Sandburg has used an unusual arrangement of free-verse lines—some long, some repetitious, and some short, sharp lines. How does this variation give added force to the ideas the poet is expressing?

23. "A Summer Night," like "Chicago," is written in free verse; yet there are definite differences in technique. List at least two of these differences and try to relate them to the poets' purposes.

24. "Stars," by Sara Teasdale, could be thought of as a religious expression. Interpret the poem from this standpoint.

25. In "Silver" and "The Waning Moon," there is a difference in the way each poet responds to the moon. Describe the ways in which the poets differ.

26. The two poems "Who Has Seen the Wind?" and "Do you Fear the Force of the Wind?" are very unlike in the pictures they present. Which poem in your judgment makes the more important comment about the wind? Explain your choice.

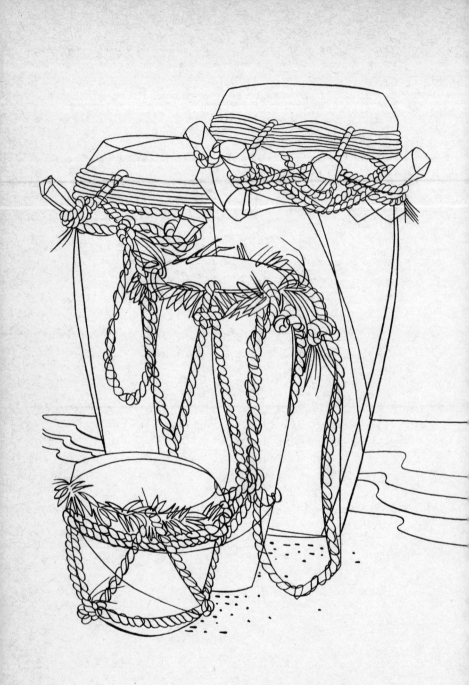

CHAPTER TEN
Looking Behind the Words

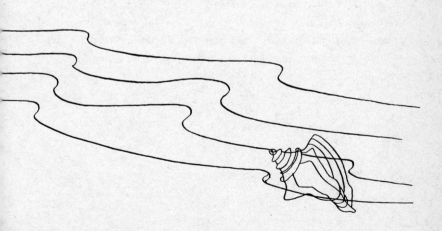

From time to time in these pages you have met the words "rhythm" and "meter." You no doubt have a general idea of the meanings of these words as applied to poetry, but perhaps you would like to have a more precise understanding of just how the poet constructs his compositions. Knowing the "rules" will help you to be more aware of the thought and planning that go into poetry. Then, too, in writing poetry yourself, you will find it a good idea to be informed about the mechanics of the craft, or your verse will often turn out to be less smooth and graceful than you would like.

RHYTHM IN POETRY

Rhythm in poetry is similar to rhythm in music. In music there is a certain basic "beat" that runs through the whole number. When you are listening to music, you are aware of the rhythm, although you are not always consciously counting it out. Music in which the beat is very obvious soon becomes tiresome, and good musicians are careful, while keeping the rhythm regular, not to let it become heavy and monotonous. Rhythmic poetry is much like music in that the poet decides in advance what arrangement of beats he is going to use and holds rather closely to his decision throughout his poem.

You may not have noticed it, but most English words have a kind of built-in rhythm. Take, for instance, the word *surprise*. When you pronounce it, you automatically give it a certain rhythm. It has an unaccented (light) syllable, *sur,* followed by an accented (heavy) syllable, *prise*. There are many words that have this rhythm:

> de*light*
> for*get*
> di*vide*

Another group of words has the accented syllable first and the unaccented one second. The following words are examples of this group:

> *pret*ty
> *com*ing
> *high* school

Not all words have just two syllables, of course. There are three- (or more) syllable words,

> under*stand*
> intro*duce*

as well as one- and two-syllable words that seem to go together to make a phrase:

> by the *way*
> of con*cern*

Notice that these examples show two unaccented syllables followed by an accented one.

When this pattern of accents is turned around, and the strong or stressed syllable is placed first, it fits such words as these:

> *nat*ural
> *study*ing
> *hap*pily
> *step* on it
> *pret*ty one

Almost all English poetry is built on these four variations of accents. Each one has a special name and is referred to as a poetic "foot." In the chart which follows, you will find the names of these "feet" and the system of marks generally used to indicate them. Before going any deeper into the subject of metrics, study this chart, so that you will have the basic building blocks of poetry clearly in mind.

NAME	HOW TO MARK IT	EXAMPLES	BEAT
iamb (iambic)	˘ ´	surprise the boy	ta-TUM
trochee (trochaic)	´ ˘	pretty try it	TUM-ta
anapest (anapestic)	˘ ˘ ´	understand it is here	ta-ta-TUM
dactyl (dactylic)	´ ˘ ˘	natural out of the	TUM-ta-ta

THE POETIC LINE

You are now ready to look at a line from a poem and see just how it is constructed. The first thing to notice is that the typical line is made up of a certain number of feet, usually all of the same type. To make it easy to see the structure, it is customary to put a ˘ mark above the unaccented syllables and a ´ mark above the accented syllables. Here is an example:

Iambic   The sea is calm tonight

You easily recognize the three feet in this line—all of them alike— as iambic. You will also notice that a poetic foot is sometimes made up of more than one word, as in "the sea." A child, just learning to read poetry, might exaggerate the rhythm and read it something like this:

The SEA is CALM toNIGHT

This exaggeration is a little hard on the listener, but it shows that most people, even the very young, have a sense of the rhythm of poetry.

The example given above is made up of the most common of all poetic feet, the iambic foot. You will find it used more than the other basic building blocks, probably because the English language seems to be iambic by nature. However, you will often find poets using the trochee, which is accented in the opposite way from the iamb. Here is a line made of trochaic feet:

Trochaic   Then the little Hiawatha

When you analyze it, it shows its structure like this:

Thén the | lít-tle | Hí-a | wa-tha

To keep the individual feet separated, it is wise to place a long vertical stroke between each of the feet. You find, in this line, four trochaic feet. It would be rather difficult to read it with any other accent without its sounding very unnatural. Once again, you see the care with which a poet must choose his words and arrange them so that there is a regular rhythm in his lines.

The third of the four major poetic feet is the three-syllable anapest. As an example, look at this line:

Anapestic   For the Angel of Death spread his wings on the blast

When you scan it as an anapestic line, it looks like this:

For the Án | gel of Death | spread his wings | on the blast

You won't find the anapest nearly so often as the iamb and the trochee. Usually it is mixed in with iambic or trochaic feet to give a line some variety of accent, but sometimes a whole poem will be based on the anapest, as is Byron's "The Destruction of Sennacherib," from which the illustration was taken.

The last of the most common poetic feet is the dactyl, the reverse of the anapest. Some of you may remember the opening line of Longfellow's "Evangeline":

Dactylic This is the forest primeval; the murmuring pines and the hemlock

Marking the dactyls, you will find this construction:

Thís ĭs thĕ | fór-est prĭm | év-ăl; thĕ | múr-mŭr-ĭng | pínes ănd thĕ | hém-lŏck

(*Note:* Meter includes *number* of feet also.)

The "meter" (that is, the rhythmic construction or pattern) of a series of dactylic feet gives a kind of swinging rhythm that is enjoyable to read and hear. It is not often, however, that you will find a poem written completely in this type of poetic foot. And you have probably noticed that even the example given is not purely dactylic; the final foot is a trochee.

VARIETY IN RHYTHM

This variation of poetic feet within a line illustrates a point that is very important to the understanding of the poet's craft: the good poet seldom sticks to precisely the same meter throughout a poem. He varies the meter here and there so that the reader will not become tired of the same rhythmic pattern. How he decides to change the pattern is solely his decision. Poetry can be analyzed and explained to a certain point, but it can never be made into a science. Just as the poet creates pictures in your imagination, so he also creates "music" with his words and rhythms. Thus poetry is a skillful combination of control and variety; and it is the writer's sense of judgment and a feeling for what is "right" that make the good poet.

With these facts in mind, examine a well-known line from English poetry and see how the poet varies his meter to give additional appeal to what he is saying. Here is the opening line of "The Highwayman," by Alfred Noyes:

The wind was a torrent of darkness among the gusty trees

To make the meter clear, one can write it like this:

Thĕ wínd | wăs ă tór | rĕnt ŏf dárk | nĕss ă-móng | thĕ gús | tў trées

You will see that, although the predominant rhythm of the line is anapestic, there are three iambic feet. The important point is that the poet achieves his variety by using two different *poetic feet,* not by ignoring his metrics altogether. In other words, poets have a certain amount of freedom, but even this freedom is governed by the requirements of poetic rhythm.

The reason for your studying these matters is not to make you an expert in analyzing the metrics of poetry, but to help you become aware of the forces that separate poetry from prose. There is something to be said for knowing the rules that govern any activity. The excitement and action of a football game, for example, take on much more meaning if you know the regulations. In the reading of poetry, the same principle applies. Being able to see beneath the surface of the poetic line will make your enjoyment greater because you know what is going on.

POETRY AND PROSE

Now that you have some knowledge of the mechanics of a line of poetry, it might be interesting to see exactly how metrical poetry is different from prose. Here is a line of prose "scanned" (analyzed) in the same way as the lines from the poems:

Thĕ treés shoŏk frŏm thĕ stróng gŭsts ŏf wínd thăt blĕw thăt níght.

You notice immediately that this line lacks the picture-producing power of the line from Alfred Noyes' "The Highwayman," quoted above. You can readily see another basic difference: there is no pattern to the stressed and unstressed syllables. Even though Noyes allowed himself some freedom in his accents, he stayed within a rhythmic pattern, and it is not hard to find the regular poetic feet in the structure. The prose line, on the other hand, contains a mixture of accented and unaccented syllables without any pattern or regularity. It is a perfectly good line of prose, but it is not poetry.

CAN YOU SCAN?

For a little practice in picking out the meter of poetry, here are a few lines from well-known poems with which you may work. See whether you can scan these lines, using the symbols in the chart.

(1) It was the schooner Hesperus
        That sailed the wintry sea;

(2) It was many and many a year ago
        In a kingdom by the sea,

(3) Jenny kissed me when we met,
        Jumping from the chair she sat in;

(4) Half a league, half a league,
        Half a league onward.

THE LENGTH OF THE LINE

There is one other technical matter you should know about in analyzing poetic lines. You may already have noticed that some lines are longer than others, but that a poet usually keeps most of the lines within any one poem about the same length. It works out in this way because, once he has decided what kind of metric foot he is going to use, the poet sticks fairly close to the same number of these feet in each line. To make it more convenient to talk about line length, there are some special terms. Here is a chart of the words that describe the length of lines found most frequently:

NUMBER OF FEET	NAME
1	monometer
2	dimeter
3	trimeter
4	tetrameter
5	pentameter

These words may appear complicated at first, but you will see that they all end in "meter," which in this case means "measure"; the first part of the words indicates the number of these "measures" to be found in the lines. So, just as a *tri*cycle has three wheels, a *tri*-meter is a poetic line with three feet in it. Here is an example of such a line:

Come spend | this day | with me

It is made up of three iambic feet, and so its full, high-sounding title is "iambic trimeter." One of the lines you examined earlier

For the An | gel of Death | spread his wings | on the blast

is made up of four anapests. Therefore, its full name would be "ana-pestic tetrameter."

The most common of all poetic lines in English poetry is that which is composed of five iambic feet. Here is an example:

For fools | rush in | where an | gels fear | to tread.

Most of the great poets of the past wrote in "iambic pentameter" much of the time, and it is still widely used by modern poets.

You will sometimes come across poetry that is hard to analyze according to the rules you know. Some poets seem to defy these regu-lations. But the great majority of the poems that you have read and will be reading are written according to the patterns you have learned, and your enjoyment will be increased because you under-stand these principles.

BLANK VERSE

Sooner or later you will hear the term "blank verse" used, and you may wonder what it means. It is really very simple. There are two characteristics to blank verse:

(1) The lines do not rhyme (that is, the rhyme is "blank" or non-existent).

(2) Each line contains five feet, all—or nearly all—iambic.

In other words, blank verse is unrhymed iambic pentameter. Shakespeare wrote most of his famous plays in blank verse. This quotation from *The Merchant of Venice* is an illustration:

> The qua | li-ty | of mer | cy is | not strained,
> It drop | peth as | the gen | tle rain | from heav'n
> Up-on | the place | be-neath: | it is | twice blessed,
> It bless | eth him | that gives | and him | that takes:

One reason Shakespeare used this form so much in his plays is that it comes close to the natural sound of everyday speech, and yet it has a rhythm to it that gives it a poetic quality. You might not be able to speak so beautifully as the people in Shakespeare's plays, but with a little practice you could learn to talk in blank verse:

> The test today in English wasn't bad,
> Although I dropped a point or two because
> I couldn't think of who it was that said:
> "To err is human, to forgive, divine."

FREE VERSE

"Free verse" is a form of poetry in which the ordinary rules of line length and strict metrical regularity are relaxed somewhat. You may remember that in Chapter One it was mentioned that free verse permits the poet to use the inner rhythm of the language to gain a great degree of "naturalness" in his expression.

It would be wrong, however, to think that the word "free" means there are no restrictions to be concerned about. In some ways free verse is harder to write than metrical verse, because there are fewer rules to serve as guides. It is a form in which the poet's sense of what is "right" is very important. Many people think that only an experienced writer can produce free verse of high quality, because so much depends on the author's "feel" for the sounds of words and phrases. On the other hand, there are those who think that free verse is a fine way for young people to express their thoughts and observations poetically. It certainly seems true that many students have a sensitivity for the language that allows them to write very expressively, and free verse appeals to them because of its leniency toward rigid regulations.

Here is an example of free verse by one of America's best-known poets, Walt Whitman:

WHEN I HEARD THE LEARN'D ASTRONOMER

When I heard the learn'd astronomer,
When the proofs, the figures, were ranged in columns before
    me,
When I was shown the charts and diagrams, to add, divide,
    and measure them,
When I sitting heard the astronomer where he lectured with
    much applause in the lecture-room,
How soon unaccountable I became tired and sick,
Till rising and gliding out I wander'd off by myself,
In the mystical moist night-air, and from time to time,
Look'd up in perfect silence at the stars.

—WALT WHITMAN

You see immediately in this poem the less regular meter, the lack of rhyme, and the general freedom with which the poet expresses himself. But you also must sense the quiet, natural rhythm of the language and the power of the words.

If free verse interests you and you would like to know more about it, turn to Chapter Eleven and you will find a section devoted to this technique. Should you have any desire to write poetry yourself, this may be the form you can begin with most easily.

CONCLUSION

This introduction to the technical side of poetry is not intended to make you an expert in analyzing how a poem is constructed. It is offered with the hope that a little knowledge of the mechanics of the poet's art will increase your reading enjoyment and prepare you to write good poetry yourself. If you wish to know more about meter, rhyme, verse form, and other technical matters that the poet must consider, your teacher will be glad to help you, and to recommend books in which these matters are discussed more completely.

There is one last statement that should be made about poetic form and meter, however, and it applies to the poetry you read in this book or in any other book: the *form* of a poem gives shape and emphasis to the thoughts of the poet, but the form is best when it is least obvious. Form in poetry can be compared to the camera technique used in filming a motion picture. The camera makes it possible for you to see the action and to understand the emotions of the actors, but if the cameraman tries to be too clever, you begin to notice his tricks and to be distracted from the story. Humorous verse depends partly on your noticing the cleverness of the meter and the rhyme, just as some motion pictures amuse you through odd, unexpected camera effects; but serious poetry, like a serious film, appeals to you because its message comes to you plainly and clearly, without distracting tricks and devices. It is wise to remember this idea when you read poetry, and important to bear it in mind when you write poetry.

CHAPTER ELEVEN

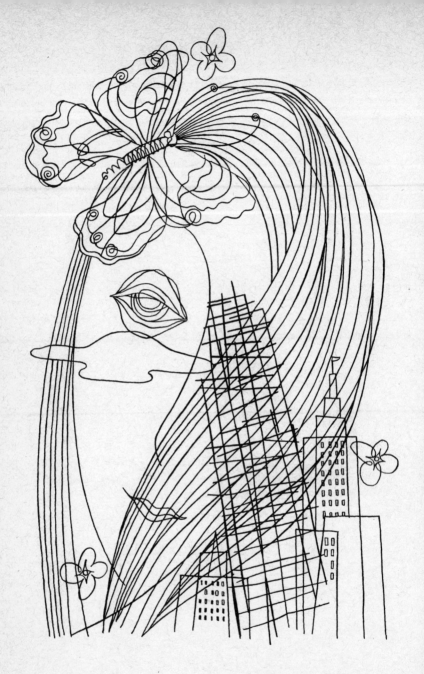

Write It Yourself

> The day was hot
> And still.
> The earth was gold,
> Ready for harvest.
> Man,
> Playing with the elements,
> Had won—this hand—
> And was quickly raking up his gains
> Before nature dealt again.
>
> —SUSAN M. STEVENS

As you have been reading the selections in the preceding pages, you may have had the urge to try your own hand at writing poetry. The poem at the top of this page was written by a student of about your age who felt just such an impulse. In Chapter One, you may remember, it was stated that the heart of poetry is in the fresh, new way of looking at familiar things or ideas. Many of the poems you have read were about subjects you know well, but the poets have responded to them in original, imaginative ways. Part of being a poet is to be able to feel things with the excitement that young people know. Adults often seem to lose this knack as they grow older, and they depend on the poet to help them recapture it. You may not believe it, but there is a great deal to be said for being young, as any poet will tell you.

In the minds of many people, the word "poetry" is almost always associated with the idea of rhyme. However, you may remember poems you have read in this book that did not rhyme, and some in which the rhythm was not so regular as you had expected. In Chapter Ten the subject of free verse was discussed. This is a type of poetry in which there is no rhyme and in which the rhythm is more "natural" than in strictly regular verse. Many students have found that it is easy for them to express themselves poetically in free verse and that the pleasure they feel from actually creating their own poetry is very great.

The big problem is in getting started. It is not often that you can just sit down and produce a poem to order, especially when you are sitting in class, and everything that seems a proper subject for poetry is somewhere else. Then, too, most students feel that the rules and regulations are so complicated that there is little use in trying. The fact is, however, that the subject matter for poetry may be found any-where, even in the classroom; and in free verse, as the name implies, you are in many ways freed from the restrictions that govern other types of poetry. Writing free verse is basically a matter of doing what you feel is right.

One of the best ways to get started is to take a colorful and descrip-tive selection from some story and put it into free verse. Remember that poetic writing is sometimes present in what is usually called "prose." Often this prose just needs rearranging into a little different form to become a very respectable poem. For example, take this prose selection, which has a certain poetic quality about it:

> The golden-haired girl sat, laughing silently,
> thinking about love, her hair falling across
> her face. She smiled with her mouth, but her
> eyes were wet and her face pale, like a
> mist-filled dawn.

Just by setting this up so that the main words and phrases become separate lines, one may make a little verse:

> The golden-haired girl sat
> Laughing silently,
> Thinking about love,
> Her hair
>   falling
>   across her face.

She smiled with her mouth,
But her eyes were wet
And her face
      pale
            like a mist-filled dawn.

Now you begin to see a poem emerging. Moreover, even if a passage of prose is poetically written, one can often make it more like a poem by leaving out unnecessary words. You have noticed in much of your reading that a poet often leaves it to you to get the sense without supplying you with every single word. This is a form of "condensation," one of the characteristics of good poetry. Another way by which the poet saves words is to use such imaginative language that one or two words will *suggest* a whole picture without his having to tell you every detail. These qualities are a part of what makes poetry so remarkable—for poetry says a great deal more than the words themselves state. Of course, everyone who reads a poem will see something a little different in it, but that is part of the enjoyment.

Bearing these things in mind, see what happens to the selection when it is condensed a little and changed slightly in a few other ways:

Golden-haired, the girl sits
Laughing silently,
Thinking about love,
Her hair
      falling
            across her face.
Her mouth smiles,
But her eyes are wet,
Her face
      pale
            like a mist-filled dawn.

This is another step forward. By changing the verbs from the past to the present tense, such as changing "sat" to "sits," one makes the whole scene become less like something that *has* happened and more like something that *is* happening or *could* happen at any time. In other words, the picture is not pinned to a particular event; the event might have occurred at any time, anywhere, and will probably occur again.

Now for a final revision: by a little more rearranging, this time putting in some descriptive words—words which suggest pictures— one can see the girl even more clearly. Also, repeating certain words gives an emphasis to important ideas:

> Grain-golden in her youth
>> the girl sits, laughing silently,
> Pondering the bitter joke of love.
>> Her sunrise hair
>>> falls,
>>>> falls,
>>>>> across her gypsy eyes.
> Life-red in its fullness,
>> her mouth smiles, but her eyes,
> Her gypsy eyes are tear-wet,
>> her ivory face
>>> pale,
>>>> pale,
>>>>> like a mist-filled dawn.

With only a little rearrangement and a few additions, the original prose passage has become a free-verse poem. This is a painless way to get started in writing poetry, and even though it is partly borrowing from someone else, a good deal of originality can go into such a composition. It permits you to gain confidence, too, before you make a completely original effort.

Perhaps before you attempt to write such a poem yourself, you would like to see another example of how it is done. Here is a selection taken from "The Sword in the Stone," the opening section of

T. H. White's fine book about King Arthur, *The Once and Future King:*

> In this enormous flatness, there lived one element—the wind.
> For it was an element. It was a dimension, a power of darkness.
> In the human world, the wind comes from somewhere, and goes
> somewhere, and, as it goes, it passes through somewhere—
> through trees or streets or hedgerows. This wind came from
> nowhere. It was going through the flatness of nowhere, to no
> place. Horizontal, soundless except for a peculiar boom, tan-
> gible, infinite, the astounding dimensional weight of it streamed
> across the mud. You could have ruled it with a straight edge.
> The titanic grey line of it was unwavering and solid. You could
> have hooked the crook of your umbrella over it, and it would
> have hung there.

There are many ways in which this selection can be put into free verse.
Here is one way a student did it:

> In this enormous flatness
> There lived one element—
> > the wind.
> It was a dimension, a power of darkness.
> In the human world,
> > the wind
> Comes from somewhere
> > goes somewhere
> > > passes through somewhere—
> > > > trees,
> > > > > streets,
> > > > > hedgerows.
>
> This wind came from nowhere,
> Was going through the flatness
> > of nowhere
> > > to no place.
> Horizontal, soundless, tangible, infinite,
> > it streamed across the mud.

You could have ruled it with a straight edge.
The titanic grey line of it was unvarying,
Solid.
You could have hooked the crook of your umbrella
Over it,
And it would have
                    hung
                    there.

Perhaps you would have arranged the words differently. You might like to rewrite it and compare your version with this one or with others that your classmates might do.

Now it is time for you to try writing one of these poems without any model to follow, just using a good prose selection as a basis for your own poetic arrangement. Before you begin, however, look at the following list of *do's* and *don't's* to bear in mind as you compose free verse, or any kind of verse, for that matter.

DO

let your imagination run free. Make any additions, changes, or rearrangements that you think give a clearer or more vivid picture.

use words from your own vocabulary. Good poetry doesn't require elegant or old-fashioned words; some of the best poetry uses the simplest language in ways that arouse your imagination and emotions.

DON'T

depend too much on odd arrangements of the lines to get your effect. A very strange appearance detracts from the force of the poem; you must have a distinct purpose for whatever you do.

use out-of-date words like *thee* and *thou* and *bringest* and *cometh*. There was a time when such forms were satisfactory, but modern poetry should be in modern language.

change the natural order of words except for a very good reason. It is usually better (because it is more natural) to say "The ship glides toward the dock," than "Toward the dock glides the ship."

Keeping these suggestions in mind, try putting the following selection (also from "The Sword in the Stone") into a verse pattern. There are so many possible arrangements that it will be surprising if any two students in your group do it in the same way. It is often interesting—and instructive—to compare the different versions made by the members of your class.

Sometimes, when they [the geese] came down from the cirrus levels to catch a better wind, they would find themselves among the flocks of cumulus—huge towers of modelled vapour, looking as white as Monday's washing and as solid as meringues. Perhaps one of these piled-up blossoms of the sky . . . would lie before them several miles away. They would set their course toward it, seeing it grow bigger silently and imperceptibly, a motionless growth—and then, when they were at it, when they were about to bang their noses with a shock against its seeming solid mass, the sun would dim. Wraiths of mist suddenly moving like serpents of the air would coil about them for a second. Grey damp would be around them, and the sun, a copper penny, would fade away. The wings next to their own wings would shade into vacancy, until each bird was a lonely sound in cold annihilation, a presence after uncreation. And there they would hang in chartless nothing, seemingly without speed or left or right or top or bottom, until as suddenly as ever the copper penny glowed and the serpents writhed. Then, in a moment of time, they would be in the jewelled world once more—a sea under them like turquoise and all the gorgeous palaces of heaven new created, with the dew of Eden not yet dry.

You will, from time to time, come across paragraphs in your reading which will lend themselves to free-verse arrangement. After you have spent a little time on this sort of writing, you will feel much more like composing a truly original poem. It would be impossible to list all the things that could be the topics of free-verse poems, but just to start you thinking, here are a few which could be used or which might suggest others:

> a tree in autumn, or spring, or winter
> the wind on the lake
> the streets or the stores at holiday time
> the steelwork of a new building
> getting up in the morning
> the school grounds at lunchtime
> a touchdown run
> the moment of sunset
> smoke from the chimney
> after the rain
> sailing before the wind
> the breaking of a wave
> a cat, finishing its bowl of milk
> the last minute of class

As you have discovered, not all poetry deals with deep, profound ideas or with the beauties of nature. Several of the subjects in the above list may seem unusual topics for poems, but you must remember that poetry is a way of looking at the world around you with originality and imagination.

Once you have chosen a subject that is meaningful to you—something that you have personally experienced or that has delighted or moved you—then you need only put aside your self-consciousness and write freely and honestly about it. When your heart and your mind are working in unison, you will be writing a poem.

This section on free verse began with a student composition. It ends with another. Perhaps this verse will make you think of some event or observation in your own life that can be the basis for an interesting poem.

FOR JUST A LITTLE WHILE

Whenever we clean
And do everything up right,
And the sun is shining
So the new-washed clothes
Smell airy,
I make one extravagant deviation
From our usual stolid thrift:
I put *two* clean, cold sheets
On my bed—instead of one.

Then, in the evening, I bathe,
And scrub my face till it's shiny,
And the mirror above the sink
Is misty with steam.
And with one quick dash
I jump into bed,
Between the clean, cold,
Taut sheets.

It only lasts a moment—
Soon the cold is warm.
But how pleasant it is
To lie shivering in the dark
For just a little while.

—REBECCA DONOHOE

THE *HAIKU*

On an old oak tree
The last leaf of autumn hangs,
Waiting to be free.

This little verse is a *haiku*. Originally, the *haiku* was Japanese, and it has been the favorite verse form in Japan for centuries. Lately, poets in America and England have found that they can learn a great deal from the simplicity and brevity of the *haiku,* and they have gained much pleasure in trying to capture the same spirit in the English language. As with most things that appear very simple, much thought and effort lie behind these little poems. A close look at a *haiku* will show in what special ways it is unique.

To begin with, the general purpose of a *haiku* is to present one simple observation, and no more. The Japanese believe that a pure poetic moment occurs when you see a little picture in nature and it "registers" on your mind. You will notice in the example above that the poet is speaking of one small observation he has made. He does not talk *about* it; he does not say what thoughts it brings to mind; he does not speak of his feelings—all he does is record what he saw. In other words, you, as the poet, must describe a tiny scene almost as a camera would see it, without any of your own presence showing. Of course, you were there and you wrote down what you observed, but you never are supposed to "show." One characteristic of the *haiku,* then, is this: it is an impersonal description of one small observation.

Another reason why the *haiku* is so short is that it is designed to be spoken in a single breath. The Japanese feel that a scene of this sort should be described in no more words than you can easily speak in one breath. This also helps to explain the brevity of this verse form.

The *haiku* is more than just short, however; it is short in a particular way. When you look at it closely, you will find that it has exactly seventeen syllables. Furthermore, these syllables are divided so that the first line has five, the second has seven, and the third, five. The careful limitation and placement of the syllables might be called the "mechanics" of a *haiku*, and the idea behind it, as described above, might be called the "spirit." The graceful combining of the mechanics and the spirit is what you must try to attain.

Before you try writing one of the little poems, look once more at the example that was printed at the beginning of this section.

> On an old oak tree
> The last leaf of autumn hangs,
> Waiting to be free.

If you think about it carefully, you will see that three questions are answered. Usually, a *haiku* will make the reader aware of WHAT is the main point of interest (the last leaf), WHERE it is (on an old oak tree), and WHEN the scene is being viewed (autumn). It is a good idea to make sure you have all three of these elements in your own compositions.

The example was written by a student after only a brief introduction to the *haiku*. He chose to rhyme the first and third lines, and although this was not necessary, many writers use rhyme to make the poem hold together a little better. You can include this rhyme pattern if you choose. The main thing is to capture a momentary observation, and present it gracefully within the tight form that is required. It will not take you long to catch on, and you will be delighted with the simplicity and beauty of what you have done.

Here are a few more student *haiku* for you to use as models:

> Bubbling swiftly down
> The water heeds spring's command,
> Tumbling toward summer.

> On her agèd face
> The troubles of life are etched,
> Shadowing her smile.

The slow stream whispers
Over tarnished silver stones—
Winter is silence.

On a fragile leaf
Beads of dew slide silently;
Spring morning begins.

The moon is so rich
It sprinkles diamonds on the
Torn waves of the sea.

LIMERICKS

No matter how grouchy you're feeling
A smile is always quite healing
  It grows in a wreath
  All around the front teeth,
Thus preserving the face from congealing.

The limerick is one type of verse that is devoted entirely to humor.
Many people have at one time or another tried their hands at writing
in this funny little form. Some limericks have become so famous that
nearly everyone knows them by heart. Here is one:

There was a young man from the city
Who met what he thought was a kitty.
  He gave it a pat
  And said, "Nice little cat."
They buried his clothes, out of pity.

And another:

A diner while dining at Crewe
Found a rather large mouse in his stew.
  Said the waiter, "Don't shout
  And wave it about,
Or the rest will be wanting one, too."

249   *WRITE IT YOURSELF*

When you begin to write limericks, you must be willing to follow a definite form and rhyme arrangement. It is not hard to do this, but at first you might feel that the rules get in your way and prevent you from saying easily what you have in mind. This is a common complaint from students who are beginning to write verse, but there is at least one thing to be said for the more restricted forms of poetry: the writer must consider his thoughts very carefully and reduce them to their most important elements. Instead of looking on form as a restriction, many poets think of it as something that makes them discard unnecessary words and phrases and fit their ideas into a more compact arrangement. You will soon learn the pleasure that comes from molding your ideas to the requirements. You may even be surprised at how many words you can eliminate and how much more skillful you become in using words exactly and economically.

In the case of the limerick, there are just a few major rules:

(1) There is a definite rhythm to each line, and you should stick closely to it. Here is how the lines should go:

ta TUM—ta ta TUM—ta ta TUM
ta TUM—ta ta TUM—ta ta TUM,
ta ta TUM—ta ta TUM
ta ta TUM—ta ta TUM
ta ta TUM—ta ta TUM—ta ta TUM.

You can alter this slightly by adding an extra *unaccented* syllable to the beginning or to the end of any line, but this is about all the freedom you are allowed .

(2) The three long lines (1, 2, and, 5) must rhyme, and the two short lines (3 and 4) must rhyme. So you see, you need three words that rhyme to take care of the long lines, and two others to take care of the short ones.

Besides these two main rules, there are some minor regulations that have become more or less traditional:

(1) Most (but not all) limericks begin with the phrase

There was a _____ from _____

You do not have to use this beginning, but it is an easy one, and it is the way most limericks start out. In the first blank space you can put "young lady" or "young fellow" or "old codger" or "instructor" or anything that fulfills your purpose. In the second blank you can place the name of a town or school or anything that tells where the subject is "from." It can be a real place or an imaginary one, whatever suits your fancy.

(2) Generally, it is best to follow this pattern:

In line one, you should tell who it is you are talking about and where he is "from."

In line two, tell something about the person or describe him in some way.

Lines three and four build up whatever peculiarity you have mentioned in the second line.

In line five you round off the limerick with an unexpected and funny conclusion, based on whatever you have talked about in the first four lines.

This may sound a little complicated; so it is a good idea to study several limericks and see how they were written.

Before you begin writing, you should be particularly aware of one problem you will meet whenever you write verse with a definite rhythm to it. Many young writers do not understand how necessary it is that the accented or stressed beats in a poetic line fall on words or parts of words which are normally accented when they are pronounced. For instance, in the following line, notice how the accent marks fall on the words that you would give emphasis to, even if the line were not in verse form:

There wás a young lády from Spáin (ta TUM—ta ta TUM—ta ta TUM).

You will see that there is just the right number of *un*accented sounds between each accented sound so that the rhythm is right and natural, and forms a standard limerick line. It is just as important to keep the unaccented syllables in strict order as it is to put the accents on the right sounds. You may grow impatient sometimes with this requirement, but do not ever give up and decide it does not matter. Saying something amusing is easy; but saying it in a clever verse form is more rewarding to you, and is more fun for the reader. It lifts the humor above the level of the wisecrack.

Limericks are not exactly "poetry," but they offer some of the same problems that you will encounter when you write more serious verse, and they are good practice. You should find them fun to write, and fun to pass around among your friends. Here are a few more for you to enjoy and to examine before you try your hand at writing one:

> There once was a hermit named Green
> Who grew so abnormally lean,
> > And flat, and compressed,
> > That his back touched his chest,
> And sideways he couldn't be seen.

> There was a young man of Devizes
> Whose ears were of different sizes.
> > The one that was small
> > Was of no use at all,
> But the other won several prizes.

> There was an old man on the Rhine
> Who was asked at what hour he'd dine.
> > He replied, "At eleven,
> > Four, six, three, and seven.
> Not to mention a quarter to nine."

THE MODERN HIAWATHA

He killed the noble Mudjokivis.
Of the skin he made him mittens,
Made them with the fur side inside,
Made them with the skin side outside.
He, to get the warm side inside,
Put the inside skin side outside;
He, to get the cold side outside,
Put the warm side fur side inside.
That's why he put the fur side inside,
Why he put the skin side outside,
Why he turned them inside outside.

—ANONYMOUS

This verse is a "parody." Any of you who have read Longfellow's famous poem, "The Song of Hiawatha," will recognize the familiar rhythm and word arrangement of the original, but you will be amused at the funny picture this verse presents. Compare it with this selection from the Longfellow poem, and you will see how cleverly the writer of the parody has imitated the original:

He had mittens, Minjekahwun,
Magic mittens made of deer-skin;
When upon his hands he wore them,
He could smite the rocks asunder,
He could grind them into powder.
He had moccasins enchanted,
Magic moccasins of deer-skin;
When he bound them round his ankles,
When upon his feet he tied them,
At each stride a mile he measured!

A true parody does more than present an amusing picture. By imitating the patterns of the original poem, the parodist makes good-natured fun of the author's style; and by substituting light and frivolous subject matter for the serious ideas of the original, he robs the poet and his poem of its dignity. Sometimes a parody is written to arouse gentle laughter; sometimes, it evokes cruel, critical amusement. In either case, parody is a form of humor.

It takes a very clever writer to construct a real parody, and it requires a special kind of reader to understand it. However, there is a variation of parody that appeals to young authors and that is well within their abilities. As children, you used to think it very funny to sing the words "Here comes the bride, short, fat, and wide" to the tune of the well known "Wedding March." When you did this, you were taking the rhythm and form of something familiar and putting words to it that you thought were funny. It wasn't very original, and you now probably think it rather childish; but by applying this same principle to verse writing, you can often conceive something that is both clever and amusing. By taking as a model a poem familiar to you and your friends, and by using *its* form and *your* words, you will find it rather easy to write a verse that either praises or pokes fun at some well-known object or activity in your life.

All students have certain common experiences that make good subject matter for this sort of "parody." To illustrate, here are some stanzas taken from a longer composition in which the student-author used Coleridge's "The Rime of the Ancient Mariner" as the basis for a complaint about various annoying features of school life.

ORIGINAL	STUDENT PARODY
The ship was cheered, the harbor cleared,	The pupils cheered, the playground cleared,
Merrily did we drop	Merrily did we drop
Below the kirk, below the hill,	Into our seats, into our work,
Below the light-house top.	Into the lunchroom slop.

And now there came both mist
    and snow
And it grew wondrous cold:
And ice, mast-high, came float-
    ing by
As green as emerald.

  The ice was here, the ice was
    there,
The ice was all around:
It cracked and growled, and
    roared and howled,
Like noises in a swound!

  Down dropt the breeze, the
    sails dropt down,
'Twas sad as sad could be;
And we did speak only to break
The silence of the sea!

  Water, water, everywhere,
And all the boards did shrink;
Water, water, everywhere
Nor any drop to drink.

And then there came both tests
    and work,
And it grew wondrous hard:
Essays, ears high, came pouring
    on,
As thick as frozen lard.

  The teachers here, the teach-
    ers there,
The teachers all around:
They croaked and growled, and
    roared and howled;
They sulked about the grounds!

  Down dropped the work, the
    work dropped down,
'Twas hard as hard could be;
And over all there weighed on us
The teachers' fiendish glee!

  Homework, homework, every-
    where,
And never a time to think;
Homework, homework, every-
    where;
Our heads began to shrink.

—HILDA KOSSOFF

These examples will give you an idea of how to go about writing
parodies. There are three rules to remember when you write this kind
of verse:

(1) Choose as your model a well-known poem with a distinctive and
    familiar rhythm, so that almost anyone will immediately connect
    your version with the original. A parody of an unfamiliar poem
    is not funny to the reader.

(2) Follow the meter of the original very closely. If possible, imitate it exactly in meter, rhyme arrangement, and stanza form. The further you let yourself wander from the model, the less clever will be the result of your work.

(3) Choose your subjects from among familiar things. The success of a parody of this kind depends on how quickly and easily your readers recognize your target.

No form of verse is easy to write, and humorous verse may be the hardest of all. However, the enjoyment you will feel from having produced a really amusing composition will repay you many times over for the work, and even the work can be fun.

Conclusion

As you have read through these pages you may have begun a journey that will take a lifetime to complete. There is such an abundance of fine poetry for you to discover and enjoy that it is well you are getting an early start. Already you have learned much. You will remember the old English mead hall with its crude benches, its trophies of warfare, its rough warriors listening with pleasure to the professional poet reciting his stories. You have learned that poetry has appealed to all kinds of people for hundreds of years, and that for every reader there is some type of poetry to bring him pleasure. You have perhaps decided upon the kinds of poetry that you like best and have begun to understand why certain poems are regarded as being better than others.

It may also be that you have found enjoyment in the *sound* of poetry, in hearing it read aloud or even in reciting it yourself. This would be in keeping with the "oral tradition" which dates back to the very beginnings of spoken communication among men. You will remember that long before writing was invented, poetry was an important part of man's life.

If you studied the explanation of rhythm and meter in Chapter Ten, you have gained a better insight into the poet's craft—how the writer puts his words together with such care to gain the memorable effects he achieves. You can now better appreciate the finer points of technique which only the trained reader understands. Symbolism, allusion, meter, rhyme, rhythm—all these poetic devices are now your familiar friends.

More important than anything else in this book, however, is the poetry itself. The poems you have read may include the greatest variety of types, subjects, and moods that you have ever seen. Perhaps it has inspired you to write poetry yourself; that is why the last chapter was included—to give you a good start in the direction of creative writing. It may be that your reading has made you want to look further into some particular type of poetry or to investigate a certain poet more fully. If so, the list of books which follows will help you to find what you are looking for.

Whatever may be the ways in which you have profited from your reading, the most important single benefit that the experience will have brought to you is a deeper enjoyment of this remarkable literary form—poetry. Your life will hold many delights, but none of them will be quite like that which poetry brings. You have discovered that the poets have the ability to enlarge your world, to make it more meaningful and understandable, to make you feel more deeply and think more clearly. Above all, they offer enjoyment. The life that lies before you will be richer in countless ways if you will listen to their many voices, and if you will continue throughout the years that are ahead to look upon poetry with pleasure.

For Your Further Pleasure . . .

The books in the following list are just some of the many collections of poetry available through your library or from bookstores. With a few exceptions each book mentioned here contains poems by many authors just as *Poetry with Pleasure* gathers together poems by a large number of poets. There are some books, however, which contain the poetry of only a single writer. You can easily find a book of poems by your favorite author—just ask for it by the poet's name. Whether you choose to browse through an anthology or to read a book by a single poet, there are countless hours of pleasure awaiting you.

Adshead, Gladys L., and Duff, Annis (compilers). *An Inheritance of Poetry.* Boston: Houghton Mifflin Company, 1948.

Arbuthnot, May Hill (editor). *Time for Poetry.* Chicago: Scott, Foresman & Co., 1961.

Auslander, Joseph, and Hill, Frank Ernest (compilers). *Winged Horse Anthology.* New York: Doubleday & Company, Inc., 1949.

Benet, Rosemary, and Benet, Stephen Vincent. *A Book of Americans.* New York: Holt, Rinehart & Winston, Inc., 1933.

Bontemps, Arna (compiler). *American Negro Poetry.* New York: Hill & Wang, Inc., 1964.

Carhart, George S., and McGhee, Paul A. (compilers) *Magic Casements.* New York: The Macmillan Company, 1926.

Cole, William (editor). *The Fireside Book of Humorous Poetry.* New York: Simon and Schuster, Inc., 1959.

Cole, William (editor). *Poems of Magic and Spells.* Cleveland: The World Publishing Company, 1960.

Cole, William (editor). *Story Poems, New and Old.* Cleveland: The World Publishing Company, 1957.

Daringer, Helen Fern, and Eaton, Anne Thaxter (editors). *Poet's Craft*. New York: Harcourt, Brace and World, Inc., 1935.

de la Mare, Walter (editor). *Come Hither*. New York: Alfred A. Knopf. Inc., 1957.

Dickinson, Emily. *Poems for Youth*. Edited by Alfred Leete Hampson. Boston: Little, Brown & Co., 1934.

Grigson, Geoffrey (editor). *The Cherry Tree*. New York: The Vanguard Press, Inc., 1962.

McDonald, Gerald D. (compiler) *A Way of Knowing; A Collection of Poems for Boys*. New York: Thomas Y. Crowell Company, 1959.

Millay, Edna St. Vincent. *Edna St. Vincent Millay's Poems Selected for Young People*. New York: Harper & Brothers, 1929.

Nash, Ogden (editor). *The Moon Is Shining Bright As Day; An Anthology of Good-Humored Verse*. Philadelphia: J. B. Lippincott Company, 1953.

Parker, Elinor (editor). *The Singing and the Gold; Poems Translated from World Literature*. New York: Thomas Y. Crowell Company, 1962.

Plotz, Helen (compiler). *Imagination's Other Place; Poems of Science and Mathematics*. New York: Thomas Y. Crowell Company, 1955.

Plotz, Helen (compiler). *Untune the Sky; Poems of Music and Dance*. New York: Thomas Y. Crowell Company, 1957.

Read, Herbert (editor). *This Way, Delight*. New York: Pantheon Books, Inc., 1956.

Teasdale, Sara. *Stars Tonight*. New York: The Macmillan Company, 1930.

Untermeyer, Louis (editor). *The Golden Treasury of Poetry*. New York: Golden Press, Inc., 1959.

Index

AUTHOR INDEX

TITLE INDEX